Central Heat

Questions and Answers books are available on the following subjects:

QUESTIONS & ANSWERS

Central Heating

W. H. Johnson

Newnes Technical Books

Newnes Technical Books

is an imprint of the Butterworth Group

which has principal offices in

London, Boston, Durban, Singapore, Sydney, Toronto, Wellington

First published 1980
   Reprinted 1982, 1983

British Library Cataloguing in Publication Data

Johnson, William Harold
   Central heating. – (Questions & Answers).
   1. Dwellings – Heating and ventilation
   I. Title II. Series
   697'.03   TH7461   79-41332

   ISBN 0-408-00459-2

Photoset by Butterworths Litho Preparation Department
Printed in England by Whitstable Litho Ltd, Whitstable, Kent

Contents

PREFACE

Not only huge price rises, but actual physical shortage of oil, remind us that we can no longer use energy thoughtlessly. We must try to use the least amount of fuel, of any kind, to create comfortable conditions indoors. We may have to reconsider how we define comfort, and we must certainly give thought to operating efficiency, for that is the key, both to getting more for less and also to paying less for what we get. In our view efficiency comes first, and will be mentioned wherever relevant in the text.

The subject of domestic heating, with its many branches, does not lend itself to being boxed into watertight compartments. Answers often overlap into other territories, and the reader is advised to make full use of the index to trace particular items of information. It will be found that more room is given to wet systems and boilers than to other forms of heating. This merely reflects the present state of the market, which changes but slowly.

This is the first book of its kind, dealing with all forms of fuel equally, but which has found it necessary to warn readers that they may not have free access to one particular fuel — ever. This is one of the facts of life. It adds point to the message that we must warm ourselves wisely, that we can afford no longer to be generous to ourselves where energy is concerned.

The object of the book is to be helpful. We scorn the pedantry of those who would claim that electric storage radiators are not 'central', and indeed we have wandered even further from convention than that, as you will see.

W.H.J.

1

INSULATION

What is the first step towards central heating?

Insulate. You have a duty to the nation, the world, and most important to yourself, to give priority to good and thorough insulation.

What does insulation do?

House insulation reduces heat loss from the house. Central heating is nothing more than a system for replacing lost heat. So the more you prevent heat loss, the less heat you will use, and the less it will cost you to replace it.

How is heat lost?

Some knowledge of the mechanics of heat transfer is a great help in preventing heat loss. The fundamental fact is that heat travels from a zone of high temperature to one of lower temperature, just as water flows down hill. Heat travels in one of three ways: conduction, we can ignore here; convection, which is the conveying of warmth by the movement of warmed air, is at least a part of all heating systems, and it is the whole of some, convectors for example; radiation, which, like light, travels in straight lines, is obviously not used to 'central' heat, but its importance cannot be overstressed. You might say that an ounce of radiant heat is worth a pound of convected heat, and we shall be coming back to this.

1

Can I install the heating system first, and later the insulation?

Quite inadvisable. Not only will you be putting in a heating system far bigger and costlier than you will need, it will cost more than it should to run, because, at the lower load after insulating, it will in most cases run less efficiently.

Is insulation expensive?

With the probable exception of proprietary double glazing it is in proportion to other costs, and, in any case, will in effect pay for itself. Compare the cost of insulation with the cost of a heating system: a heating system has an insulation cost and a running cost and a running cost. Insulation not only has no running cost but it actually achieves a saving by reducing heating costs, which will pay off its installation cost in, in some cases, only three or four years. The paying off time will get less as fuel prices continue to rise.

Can I do my own insulating?

The only item which cannot be done without the special plant and equipment of the contractor is cavity wall insulation. For this you should employ a firm which is a member of the National Cavity Insulation Association. Other insulation work makes varying demands upon the skills which many posses. Bad doors and windows, for instancr, sometimes need joinery work. Double glazing materials are sold in kit form.

What is the order of priorities in insulating?

Most heat is lost through the house walls. But the most cost effective insulation , i.e. the cost per unit of heat saved, is that in the roof. The two aspects are illustrated in Figs. 1.1 and 1.2.

How do I insulate the loft?

If the loft is not used as part of the living space, simply unroll mineral wool or glass fibre to be a snug fit between the joists.

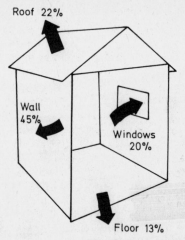

Figure 1.1   Heat loss from a house

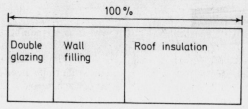

Figure 1.2   Cost effectiveness of insulating a house

Tuck in the ends so that any wind entering at the eaves cannot blow under the blanket. Do not lay insulation under cisterns. Instead, turn up the edges to cover the sides of the cistern(s) and hold it in position with wire or wire netting. Make a wooden lid and cover this with a piece of the same blanket. See Fig. 1.3.

Any pipes which are in the loft, if they lie near the floor, should be included in, i.e. covered by, the rolled out blanket.

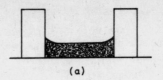

(a)

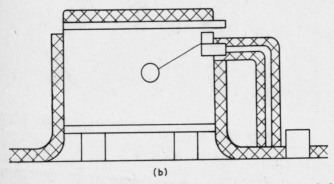

(b)

Figure 1.3   Insulation in the roof space: blanket insulation (a) tucked between joists. (b) The cold water cistern is contained within the insulated space. Wire netting holds the insulation in place

Pipes which are too high to be so treated must be wrapped, either with proprietary pipe lagging or with a felt type material. Carpet underfelt is suitable.

An alternative to blanket type insulation is loose fill vermiculite, a fine scale-like material which is poured in and raked smooth and level. It has one advantage in that it does not irritate the skin if handled without gloves. However, it should not be used if any wind blows through the attic.

In both cases, loose fill and blanket, the economic thickness, i.e. the best balance between doing a good job and not paying excessively for it, is 100 mm or 4 in. This, with blanket, may mean more than one layer, each carefully tucked in.

4

What do I do if I use my attic as living space?

Obviously you do not want to cut off the heat supply beneath you. In this case you must apply your insulation to the pitch of the roof. This calls for a different type of material, a rigid board type. If the roof is close boarded under the slates or tiles, it is safe to form a cavity, using a rigid material such as hardboard on the face of the roof timbers, and fill the cavity with mineral wool, glass fibre or vermiculite (Fig. 1.4).

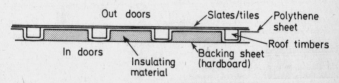

Figure 1.4   Section through a roof 'sandwich'

If the roof lacks close boarding, and is perhaps simply slates which seem to be in good condition, it would be better to use a rigid material which is itself the insulator. A proprietary board such as Asbestolux would do. Or you might use, say, a softboard, and fix to the inner (attic room) side a second insulator such as expanded polystyrene tiles. If the roof is not in good condition it should receive attention before being permanently hidden away behind a boarded cover.

Do floors lose heat?

The floor heat loss of 13% shown in Fig. 1.1 relates to a suspended timber ground floor. The free circulation of air beneath such a floor should never be curtailed. Although insulation may be applied under a timber floor, as shown in Figs.1.5 and 1.6, it is advisable to have the under-floor treated for dry rot and woodworm before proceeding. (Such treatment is beneficial in any case.) It is only the *ground* floor which requires insulation, even in blocks of flats.

Floors lose heat in two ways. There is the removal, in the same way as walls and ceilings act, by becoming warmed, conducting the heat through and giving it to the cold air on the other side. But floor boards quite often allow cold air to pass upwards through joints and cracks, and through imperfect marrying to skirting boards. These draughts must be stopped.

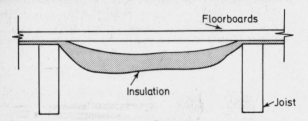

Figure 1.5   Ground floor insulation, new dwellings

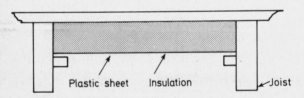

Figure 1.6   Ground floor insulation, existing dwellings

They can be stopped at source by filling the cracks with papier maché, sanded down when dry. Or they can be stopped, with part insulating, by covering the whole floor with close fitting hardboard. Ordinary grade will do if a further floor covering is to be used, and it is desirable, for insulation's sake, to add both underfelt and carpet. If there is no carpet, the use of heavy quality mats will help. It should be remembered that every bit of insulation helps. A floor half insulated is already half as good as one wholly insulated.

How important is double glazing?

Going back to Fig. 1.1, we find windows debited with 20% heat loss, which is very much an average. Despite irresponsible advertising, it is necessary to appreciate that even the best double glazing will do no more than reduce this to 10%, or half what it was. For most houses heat loss through windows is not a major item, though undoubtedly important. But windows are a special case in having, as single glazed units, a very high rate of heat loss. And this gives rise to a cold descending current of air — a 'cold draught' — and very often to condensation, which can cause mould formation among other troubles.

Condensation is in part due to bad ventilation, to be mentioned later, and double glazing is not an automatic cure though it will undoubtedly reduce it.

Should one double glaze?

For two reasons, cold draught and condensation, it is desirable. The point must be made, however, that unless double glazing is done well there is little point in doing it at all.

How should we double glaze?

If you feel able to afford proprietary units, we suggest employing a member firm of the Insulation Glazing Association. Remember that the best units are sealed by some means, not provided with a drain hole: the gap should be in the region of 18–22 mm or ¾ in, not 4½ in which is fine for sound insulation but not much use for heat (Fig. 1.7). The aim is to create a thin sandwich of still dry air, and this must be borne in mind if you make your own. The type which relies upon a sliding glass panel has a limited value as an insulator for heat, though it may have other advantages, for instance being able to open the window.

Attaching a second pane to a wooden framed window is not difficult. If the frame is in good condition it may be possible

7

to effect a seal using double sided Cellotape, then holding the whole in place with wooden fillets, like a thin picture frame. But a moulded framing costs very little, and is often advertised as a kit, with specially designed fastening down pieces, in one of the d.i.y. magazines.

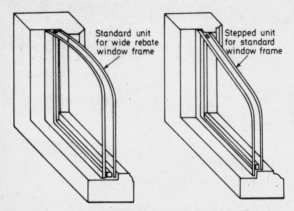

Figure 1.7   Types of double glazing (Pilkington Bros Ltd)

Metal framed windows present more problems. It may mean that you have to drill and tap the frame at intervals in order to attach whatever you choose as a glass retaining material. If this proves too much of a job, you might consider the framed panel which is made to fit the entire window embrasure, and is put into position when required.

Is there no alternative to double glazing?

Taking into account that we still expect the coldest weather in winter time and that during the winter the hours of darkness exceed the daylight hours, we can quite simply achieve a high degree of protection, not only for the greater part of the time, but at that time of day which for most of us is when we need it.

The answer is: curtains. Heavy quality curtains, preferably lined, and just that much bigger than the window area so that they will tuck in well at sides and bottom and effectively seal off the window so that the warm air from the room cannot reach it. A well fitting piece of hardboard or cardboard slipped in first adds even more to the protection. A pelmet with a top takes care of the upper end.

What else needs attention?

We have already mentioned the possibility that joinery may be needed. But in most cases the tackling of draughts, which is the next step, can be done by using proprietary draught sealing strips, and sometimes by homemade remedies — anything to stop the unwelcome entry of cold air, or the equally unwelcome escape of warmed air.

The biggest escape of all, in many houses, occurs by the chimney. This is simply a large hole in the house. The ordinary chimney, with an open fire in it, can carry away ¼ ton of air an hour, which you have probably paid to warm. The uncontrolled open fire is no friend of the cost conscious householder, and must be controlled. It is essential to fit a throat controller wherever there is a solid fuel appliance at work. This, similar to the old type register, can be adjusted from shut to open, to a position where the 'pull' on the fire is just positive. Closed a little from there, the fire smokes, which is the easy way to adjust it. Controlled draught leads to greater efficiency and saves running cost. Advice on these matters can be obtained from the Solid Fuel Advisory Service, whose local representative is probably the fuel supplier.

What about ventilation?

This is essential, but must be controlled for best results. In the larger rooms in the house, after insulation, it should not be necessary to shut doors. Free circulation, plus the air which will enter through opening an outer door for example, will take care of normal ventilation requirements. In extreme cases, where the house is practically sealed, a means of air entry, e.g. via air bricks with adjustable dampers, may be needed.

9

Wherever there is a fossil fuel appliance (gas, oil or solid fuel stove, boiler etc) connected to a conventional flue, there is a need for a purpose-made air entry point. If the house ventilation is already suited to the inhabitants, this special air

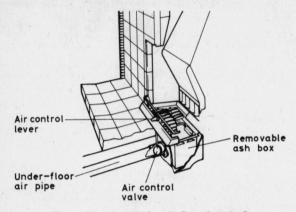

Air control lever

Removable ash box

Under-floor air pipe

Air control valve

Figure 1.8   A typical underfloor draught fire

entry may be directed straight to the appliance. The under-floor draught system of Baxi is an example. Alternatively, a ventilator may be let into an outside wall, and a duct run from it to a point near the appliance. (Fig. 1.8). The *minimum* size of air opening is specified by the fuel authority concerned.

A special need for ventilation occurs in three rooms: the toilet, bathroom and kitchen. All three should have a vent to outdoors. The kitchen in particular may benefit from an electrically operated extraction fan. But if a fan is fitted, ask the gas authority to check that it is not robbing any gas appliance fitted there. A larger air intake may be needed. The most difficult case is the bedroom in which condensation occurs on the window, even on walls. If any double glazing is done it should begin here. But in terms of ventilation, some rooms are not situated to take advantage of natural air circulation. A certain cure, and not as complex as it might seem, is one which automatically keeps the moisture-in-air level just below the point at which condensation will occur. The cure consists in having a small extraction fan fitted, and controlled by a humidistat. This eliminates the condensation bogey with the minimum loss of air from the house, and promotes air change in the room as a bonus.

Cavity wall insulation was mentioned, but my walls have no cavity. Can I insulate?

You have a choice, and if you could choose both you would be very well served. You can insulate your walls outside, by a protective cover. Slate hung, tile hung or barge boarded walls are sheltered from the cooling effects of wind and rain, and there is a small air pocket behind the cover.

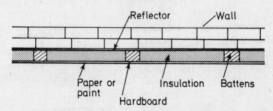

Figure 1.9   Plan view of insulated wall

What are called thermal inner linings act very differently, since they keep warmth away from the wall. Rooms so treated warm up much more quickly than even those with cavity lining. There is however some risk of moisture penetration since no warmth passes through to repel it. The wall should be treated externally, in dry weather, with a waterproofing liquid. A thermal inner lining material often used is expanded polystyrene tiles or sheet. Fireproofed grade should be used. The tiles may be given any required decorative wall treatment.

A more effective treatment consists of fitting vertical battens, 1×1 in, to the wall at about 600 mm (2 ft) centres (Fig. 1.9). Before attaching hardboard to these battens, fill the gap about to be formed with mineral wool or glass fibre. A dab of

11

adhesive will hold the wool or fibre to the wall during construction. If the wall is first lined with cooking foil as a reflective insulator, so much the better.

How can we choose the best insulating material?

You start by choosing among those which are of the correct type. The most obvious difference lies in whether they are rigid or not. A rigid material is self-supporting and will not sag or collapse if not supported. A non-rigid material, of which the clearest example is vermiculite, must be wholly supported.

Another area of choice would concern its location. If there is a chance that it will get wet, for instance, or be exposed to influences which would cause it to become 'lousy', avoid materials which are natural. In the list below hair felt, cork and probably fibre board, could support mould and livestock in certain conditions. Artificial or mineral products would not.

After that, you are free to choose according to value for money, i.e. price and insulating value. The table gives a few examples of the latter, by quoting thermal conductivity. The important thing about this table is that the lower numbers are best for insulation. Remember that these are unit thicknesses. For example, if you double the thickness of insulation you will halve (roughly) the heat loss.

Insulating material	Conductivity ($W/m\,^{\circ}C$)
Slag (mineral) wool	0.042
Granulated cork/bitumen slab	0.042
Sheet cork	0.084
Vermiculite	0.067
Hair felt	0.040
Fibre board	0.059
Glass silk mat	0.040
Glass fibre	0.036
Air	0.026
Polystyrene (expanded)	0.033

Which is most suitable for wet conditions?

None. Insulating materials must be, and stay, dry.

2

CENTRAL HEATING SYSTEMS

What is central heating?

In this book, central heating is a convenient name for any form
of heating other than single room appliances. The effect of
central heating is to bring to the household generally a greater
standard of comfort with economy. It is becoming less and less
tied to centrality, more to evolving common sense and
experience. To think in any other terms is to do the public a
grave disservice and deny them access to important recent
developments.

What systems are available?

Broadly, there are *wet* systems and *dry* systems. The wet systems
depend upon water circulating around to convey the warmth
created in a central boiler. All other systems are dry. These
include warm air, circulated in much the same way as water,
and electric storage radiators, and convectors not on a wet
system. We shall deal with them separately.

What are the advantages of a wet system?

Water has a very high capacity for holding heat. An entire
medium sized room can be warmed by water in a ½ inch
pipe. Consequently it is not obtrusive in the house. For that

reason it can always be added to an existing house without trouble.

The boiler which heats the water for the heating circuit will heat the domestic hot water as well.

What are the disadvantages of a wet system?

Water is a bad enemy. If the system is not water tight, the result can be very messy.

Water is the universal solvent, and brings with it substances which, according to the source of the water, are frequently either scale forming or corrosive. The use of indirect systems has in part mitigated these effects, but the persistence of the cast iron boiler shows that it is still recognised to be a problem.

What are the advantages of a dry system?

Water is not involved. In a ducted warm air system, any leaks in the low pressure circulating air system are harmless. Air (which is the heating medium whatever the source of heat) does not corrode the apparatus. A ducted warm air system usually includes an air filter to remove air borne dust. It can become the nucleus of an air conditioning system, in simple form.

What are the disadvantages of a dry system?

Air has a low capacity for heat, and in ducted systems the ducts must be very large, e.g. 150×200 mm (6×8 in) is common. Ducted systems can rarely be accommodated in an existing house, because of their size, without being obtrusive.

Non-ducted systems, e.g. electric storage radiators, rely upon nature to distribute the warm air output, which always seeks to rise.

It must be added that ducted warm air systems are rarely installed by householders, in part because they usually go into houses under construction, in part because they offer practical problems to amateurs.

14

Do all good dry systems need ducts?

Only that system which propels warmed air to the precise points at which it is delivered into rooms needs ducts.

There is a convenient half-way system which relies upon stub ducts. These are short ducts of low resistance which deliver warmed air to two or more fairly adjacent areas, whence it is left to circulate.

The majority of dry systems do not have any use for ducting. They are room heaters of more than one kind, which purists argue are not central. But they have a claim to this when they are uniform in type and depend upon a common energy source. Semantics apart they must have a place here because they are important to domestic heating.

There is one unit, mentioned under the oil firing heading, which has no ducting, is capable of whole house heating, yet exists in one room only. It is a successor to the Roman furnace, or more recently to the so-called 'brick central'. It is a hearth mounted unit which warms enough air for the house, and open doors allow nature to do the rest.

How do electric storage heaters work?

They have a large heat reservoir, which is why they are heavy. Heat from a hot wire is put into the unit during the night hours (to suit electricity generation) and because of the heavy insulation on the unit it leaks out quite slowly, lasting at least most of the day.

Control over the amount of heat, to suit the weather, is anticipatory, i.e. you must determine the night before whether to allow more or less heat in. There is no control over the output, which is a natural leak.

There is, however, a more technically refined type of unit in which the output is controllable. This unit simply has a lot more insulation, to reduce the natural leak to very little. Output is then arranged at will, either by starting a fan, or more simply by opening an air damper. The fan is usually worked by a clock, or room thermostat, or both.

Do storage heaters resemble electric floor warming?

Electric floor warming is the same in principle as the first type of unit described, namely that one which cannot have its output controlled. There is no version comparable to the controllable unit. This type of heating served its purpose, and is best forgotten.

What is Electricaire?

This is the name given to an electric storage heater of a size much greater than required for one room. It is usually associated with a stub duct system. Given adequate fan power it can work a full duct system. It is, of course, the controlled outlet type of heater.

Does electric storage heating have any special advantages?

It must be considered an equal competitor with the others. But it can claim advantages in the following special cases.

1. Where the householder is a tenant, and paying for the installation himself. All he need leave behind is the special wiring, not a major item.
2. In cases where a moderate temperature is required continually, not just at peak times.
3. Houses left for long periods, notably the country cottage. The only other possible heat source is gas. Electricity is just preferable in being independent of such secondary items as pilot flames, heating pump or fan, and so on. Both systems require an ongoing supply of electricity. Storage heaters, which may be set quite low, give that continuous input which safeguards water pipes and keeps mould at bay. It is relevant that gas is very often not available in such cases.

Is there anything comparable to electric storage heating?

The gas industry has seen to it that there is. We now have gas fired unit heaters, currently called wall heaters. These are all for balanced flue and so can be put into any room. They are not, of course, storage heaters, that being exclusive to the electric models. But in perhaps the majority of cases the continuous function is not so valuable as the ability to turn the heating on and off at will.

Do gas fired wall heaters have any advantages?

Gas boiler manufacturers will deny strongly that these may be the heaters of the future, yet the possibility exists. They are compact, self contained, much more likely to be turned on and off than radiators are, hence more economical. They do not require wet system piping throughout the house, just a single small gas pipe. They will work at their rated efficiency practically all of the time, unlike boilers. Physiologically, they have much in common with hot water radiators and electric storage heaters, their output being a mixture of convection and radiation.

Do gas fired wall heaters have any disadvantages?

Certain houses might not look their best if punctured by a number of balanced flue terminals. These, however, are small. The principal drawback, and it may be only temporary, is that the unit is at present too simple, too elementary. We have become accustomed to having both the timing and the temperature adjustment of our home heating taken care of automatically. It is more efficient that way because controls remember to do it. These wall heaters could have external controls fitted, but not readily. This must be the next stage in their development if they are to realise their full potential.

How do dry systems cope with domestic hot water?

Since the dry systems are principally gas and electric, the domestic hot water system follows suit. It is usual for electric systems to have an immersion heater in a copper cylinder. This is a very low cost installation, with a high running cost

17

but considerable convenience. The way to cut the running cost is to arrange to have the immersion heater on the same tariff as the heating. This will mean initially having a larger than usual cylinder, since all the hot water needed must be made at night, to quality for the cheap rate.

Gas systems may be of different types. They may be storage systems, using a very small boiler of the type called a circulator, whose maximum output is just over 3 kW or 10 000 Btu/h. This imposes no restrictions upon the instantaneous rate of demand for hot water. Alternatively, gas systems may avoid using storage, and have instead an instantaneous heater piped to all hot taps. The latest models of this type of heater overcome an earlier objection, that its automatic safety devices caused it to shut down rather than supply a shower bath. But the problem of maximum demand persists, whereby the rate at which it can deliver hot water makes it rather slow in bath filling. It is, however, a very popular appliance.

Though there is no reason in principle why electric heating should not go with gas water heating and vice versa, there are often pricing advantages in, as it were, bulk buying fuel.

Does oil figure in the 'dry systems' and hot water market?

We have mentioned the large hearth convector without ducting. This unit can be fitted with a back boiler, being in many ways like a huge gas fire. There is at least one unit on the market, made by Afos Ltd, which is a combined air and water heater. As we have noted elsewhere, oil does not lend itself readily to appliances on the small scale, when full control systems are expected.

Does solid fuel combine with dry systems?

Everything is possible, but at this date there is no scope for solid fuel in a dry system which may reasonably be called a system. It is very much a matter of controls and controllability. Dry systems do not offer the same buffer facilities which are obtainable from wet systems, to absorb the run-over energy released by solid fuel after it has been ordered to slow down.

18

It is, however, well worth noting that there is a lot more to a good solid fuel room heater than flickering flames. It can make a substantial contribution to air warming, which is the principle of dry systems.

How much air warming does a solid fuel appliance do?

It is now more important than ever to see the various solid fuel appliances of the room heater type in their order of efficiency. At the bottom of the list is the old fashioned open fire, still regarded with great nostalgia by some older folk. At its best it wastes 85% of the fuel it gets, and it is rarely at its best. It achieves this ignoble result in several ways, one being that it makes next to no direct contribution to air warming. Indirectly, some air is warmed by objects which have been warmed by radiation from the fire.

A much improved open fire is now obtainable, with restricted throat and with provision for warming air which is enabled to pass over its surfaces. (We are not here complicating things by including back boiler heat recovery.)

But let us now look at the top of the list, where we have the modern closed or closeable stove. With doors closed, this has an overall efficiency in excess of 60%. That figure, too, is improved in hopper types which do not have to be opened regularly for refuelling. By all means be dissatisfied with up to 40% waste, but consider too how much improved it is compared to 85—90% waste from an open fire. With the closeable doors open, the efficiency falls. The only thing wrong with the closeable stove is psychology — public psychology. But perhaps this yearning for the flickering flame will become less intense if its cost can become well known.

Is central heating really better than having fires in every room?

The question is not entirely realistic. Only old houses have chimneys in all habitable rooms, and even these rarely in the hall. New houses may have none at all. Balanced flues (for gas appliances) need an outside wall, and a hall often lacks this. We stress the hall because of the truth of the old saying that "to "eat the 'all of the 'ouse is to 'eat the 'ole of the 'ouse".

3

WET SYSTEMS

What is a wet system?

In a wet system, water is heated in a boiler and circulated by pipework to a number of heat emitters, then, partly cooled, back to the boiler for reheating. The same boiler usually heats the domestic hot water as well.

What are heat emitters?

These are most commonly radiators. But they may be convectors, or fan convectors, or skirting heaters. See Figs. 3.1, 3.2, 3.3 and 3.4.

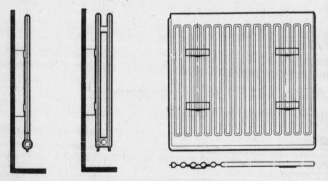

Figure 3.1   *Typical panel radiator which may be single or double panels (Thorn Heating Ltd)*

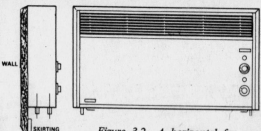

WALL

SKIRTING

FLOOR

Figure 3.2 A horizontal fan convector (Myson Group Marketing Ltd)

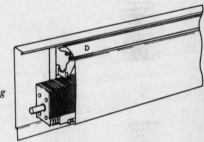

Figure 3.3 Typical skirting heater in section. D is the damper

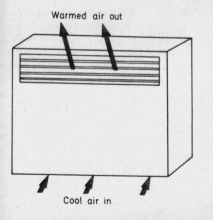

Warmed air out

Cool air in

Figure 3.4 A typical wall mounted natural convector

How does water circulate in a wet system?

Systems may be put into four categories. Gravity circulation is fine if you happen to own a cottage on the moors, with no electricity. With a coal fired back boiler you can enjoy some warmth. But for any other situation it ranks with oil lamps for cars, outdated, temperamental, sluggish and inadequate. Domestic hot water is still commonly produced by a gravity circulation, but in well defined circumstances, outlined later.

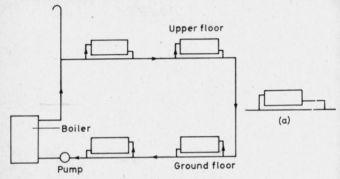

Figure 3.5   A typical single-pipe system

Next in order of precedence and age is the one-pipe small bore pumped system. The introduction of a pump or circulator, hence powered circulation, allowed drastic reductions in pipe sizes. In the one-pipe system the cooled water from the first radiator is mixed with the on-going stream, so that the second radiator receives cooler water. That is its greatest weakness, leading to the need for larger radiators for a given duty on the downstream side of each other. See Fig. 3.5.

This leads to the two-pipe system, shown in Fig. 3.6. Study of this will show that the cooled water from each radiator is led into a second pipe, called the return, and thence to the boiler. Thus each radiator receives its hot water at boiler temperature, less normal losses in transmission. This is a far better system, in terms of controllability, and size of radiator.

22

Radiators are neither beautiful nor cheap. There is, of course, more pipe to pay for, but this is partly offset by the factors mentioned.

Last we have microbore, a variant of the two-pipe system. It uses smaller tube than small bore, and requires a more

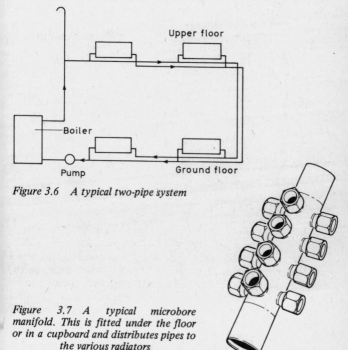

Figure 3.6   A typical two-pipe system

Figure   3.7   A   typical   microbore manifold. This is fitted under the floor or in a cupboard and distributes pipes to the various radiators

powerful pump to cause adequate circulation. (The conveyance of sufficient heat still depends upon taking enough water at high temperature to the emission appliance.) Microbore practice involves a moderately short run from the boiler to a manifold (see Fig. 3.7) in normally sized pipe. From this, out-and-home

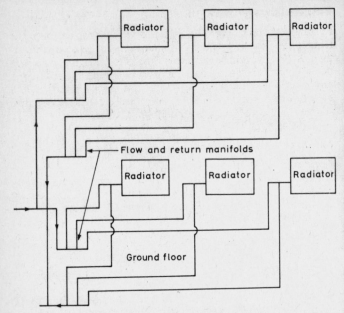

Figure 3.8   Typical microbore system showing the use of manifolds.

runs are made to each heat emitter, as shown in Fig. 3.8. Microbore pipe is usually quite flexible, and equivalent to running an electric cable.

Does microbore have all the advantages?

Not by any means! The pipe is often vulnerable to damage, being soft. The small waterway is more readily blocked by foreign matter than small bore is. Then there is the need for a larger pump. Microbore must be seen to take its place as a worthwhile member of the possible systems. It has, and will no doubt keep, a minor share of the market.

Never be tempted by price to use nylon pipe, if you choose microbore.

24

What are the snags about small bore?

Fortunately, very few. The pump, once a constant source of trouble, is now so reliable as to earn itself a guarantee for as long as two years in some cases. Thanks to pumping, pipe runs do not have to conform to 'falls' for air venting. In general, any trapped air will find its way to the top of radiators, and use of the air vent key should be standard practice. In our view the best buy is the two-pipe small bore system.

Do pipes have to be copper?

Not necessarily! But copper remains favourite. Stainless steel makes a bid for consideration and, if copper were not available, we would choose it. Mild steel tube was used but contributed its own rust to clog the works. Plastics have not yet become able to stand the temperature involved, and, as noted, the attempt to sponsor nylon pipe for microbore systems should be ignored.

Does hard water affect wet systems?

If we have a heating system only, it holds perhaps 5 to 10 gallons or 25 to 50 litres of water. This water does not change but circulates continuously. Consequently, even if the water is very hard, it contains only a very small amount of scale material which does no damage.

If the system includes provision for domestic hot water, as is most likely, then the water in the cylinder is being changed constantly, as it is used at taps. The correct procedure is to use an indirect cylinder, which contains a heat exchanger. The water for taps never itself passes through the boiler but is heated by boiler water. This is discussed in more detail in Chapter 7.

Does corrosion affect wet systems?

Some natural waters, quite the opposite to hard water, have an acid character. These can attack metals. But, as will be seen from the previous question, an indirect system will ensure that only a small and relatively harmless amount of raw water ever reaches the hottest zones, where most trouble would occur.

There are, however, other forms of corrosion. One is the so-called electrochemical effect and this occurs at the junction of two dissimilar metals, e.g. copper and steel. It tends to be set up by suitable types of water, and affects some regions more than others. There are ways of avoiding electrochemical corrosion but it would be unsafe to generalise here. Best ask either the laboratory of your local water authority or, if for instance your system has a gas boiler, ask the gas authorities for advice.

Other forms of corrosive action can occur in wet systems, in part bacterial. Hydrogen (which may be burnt) issuing from the air vent of a radiator is a sign of such a state. There are proprietary additives which claim to deal with these troubles. Again, if it happens to you, consult the fuel authority for the type of fuel you use.

Are radiators the best heat emitters?

They are certainly the most numerous. There is a wide range of choice of sizes, making it easy to match the calculated heating requirements of any room. Since heat loss depends on surface

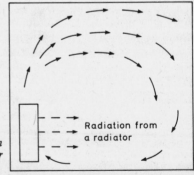

Figure 3.9 Convected warm air pattern from a radiator or natural convector

26

area, radiators can be had in a variety of height/length ratios, to suit available spaces on walls. A radiator, alone among the convectors, gives off up to half of its output as radiation. For that reason it must be seen, not hidden away behind furniture, or tucked into an alcove which screens its radiation, or baffles its convection currents, or both (Fig. 3.9).

But radiators must take their place among other heat emitters which will be mentioned shortly.

Is there more than one type of radiator?

It is very rare now to find a column radiator, usually cast iron and often on feet. This unattractive device had the advantage of cramming a large output of heat into a relatively small wall area. But its place as an alternative to the panel radiator has been taken by a small number of new designs. One, for instance, presents a solid front, of thin metal, to the back of which is welded a continuously wound coil of pipe carrying the hot water. The choice may fall on one of these for reasons of output and wall area, or appearance. Certification — will it do what is claimed? — is to be found in the MARC (Manufacturer's Association of Radiators and Convectors) approved sign and this will be found with all panel radiators and with some of the others. It should be looked for when buying. Since it is a British manufacturers' mark, it is perhaps a little unfair that there are imported radiators of great merit which cannot be so certified. But the buyer should safeguard himself.

What is the difference between radiators with connections at top and bottom?

None, so long as we are talking about pumped wet systems. It is indeed becoming more common to find radiators with both connections at the bottom simply because it makes the pipework less obtrusive. In some cases this is carried even further by having a common connection point, both inlet and outlet using the same corner of the radiator.

27

How is heat output of a radiator calculated?

It is related to the surface area, which for a single panel radiator is twice the 'picture frame' area plus extra for the profiled surface. A manufacturer's catalogue will give both surface area and heat emission for every size of panel. Double panel radiators follow the same rule but deduct a proportion from the total to allow for the fact that two of the surfaces face each other and do not therefore fulfil the second condition. This is that there shall be a temperature difference across the radiator shell, i.e. from hot water to cool air, of 55 deg C or 100 deg F.

Although the real figure varies, being greater for short radiators and decreasing as the height increases, it is sufficient to take an average figure per square metre or foot of radiator surface as follows.

Single panel,
$\quad$ $K = 0.60$ kW/m^2/55 deg C or 190 Btu/ft^2/100 deg F
Double panel,
$\quad$ $K = 0.505$ kW/m^2/55 deg C or 160 Btu/ft^2/100 deg F

Example: If the calculated heat loss from a room (see later) is 2 kW or 6 800 Btu/h, this requires a single panel radiator of area $2/0.6 = 3.3$ m^2 (36 ft^2). From a manufacturer's list a suitable one would measure 533 mm (21 in) high × 2.77 m (109 in) long or 685 mm (27 in) × 2.16 m (85 in).

List figures may be adjusted to use other values of temperature drop, multiplying by a factor from the following table.

Real temperature difference		Factor
deg C	deg F	
39	70	0.63
44.5	80	0.76
50	90	0.87
61	110	1.12
67	120	1.25

28

Are valves necessary on radiators?

Every radiator should have a valve on its inlet and outlet. One is for use as an on/off control (as in selective heating) and one, usually lockshield type, is set when balancing the system.

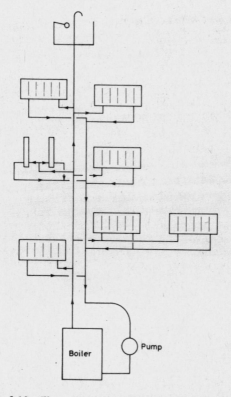

Figure 3.10   Illustrating the benefit obtained by running flow and return pipes by the most direct route. Only the radiator circuits are shown

Radiators equipped with thermostats must be treated in the same way, though the valve will be not directly connected to the radiator. The secondary purpose of the valves is to be able to isolate the radiator, for painting, repair etc, without draining down the system.

Do radiators have to be fitted under windows?

Not necessarily. If you have double glazing, there is no need. If you do not, then the under-window radiator does counteract the descending cold air. But recent measurements have shown that it does this at a price. First, the warmest air meets the coldest surface, giving greatest heat loss initially. The other factor is that a radiator against an outside wall is about 5% worse off than a radiator against an inside wall.

If you do fit a radiator under a window, do not allow it to be covered by a full length curtain.

Where is the next best place to fit a radiator?

Provided it can create a good air flow pattern, which you must visualise for yourself, almost any place will do, to suit the pipework. This leads to a very economical pipe run in some houses, particularly if they happen to be more tall than broad. Fig. 3.10 shows how the entire system can be fed off short runs from an almost straight up and down flow and return.

How are radiators supported?

Every radiator is supplied complete with adequate wall fixing brackets, designed to take the weight of the radiator full of water. If a failure should occur it is due to inadequate fixing between bracket and wall, and this detail of installation requires care.

The other important feature of the maker's wall bracket is that it ensures the radiator's distance from the wall being sufficient for normal heat output to occur. Air must pass freely up behind the radiator.

Are radiator shelves necessary?

For radiators not fitted under windows they are desirable. The rising current of warm air carries up dust and charred living organisms. These tend to settle or condense on the cooler wall surface above the radiator, causing a dark stain to occur.

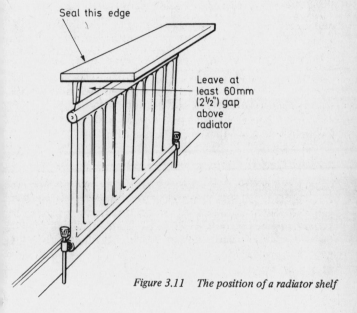

Seal this edge

Leave at least 60 mm (2½") gap above radiator

Figure 3.11   The position of a radiator shelf

The purpose of the shelf is to divert the rising air current out into the room, where its charred burden may be dispersed over a very wide area without being noticeable. To be successful a shelf must be 25 mm or so longer than the radiator at each end: 50 mm wider measured from the wall: not less than 60 mm nor more than 100 mm above the radiator: and it must be sealed with an airtight sealing strip to the wall, to prevent air from escaping up behind it (Fig. 3.11).

Does a reflector plate behind a radiator improve efficiency?

It does not improve the efficiency of the radiator. It has two rather different effects. It reduces the amount of heat which is transmitted and probably lost through the back wall, which we have seen can be up to 5%. But it also reduces the total output of the radiator by a small amount, because it throws some of the heat output back into the radiator. If the radiator is of ample size for the job, a plate can be mildly beneficial.

Are radiators affected by the type of water system used?

We have noted that in single pipe systems, radiator size pro rata has to be increased as we move downstream, to allow for falling water temperature. This alone is an argument in favour of 2-pipe systems. But there is a type of radiator for which a 2-pipe system is compulsory. This is the type which has a high resistance to flow, generally because the water has to pass through a copper tube. In a single pipe system, the radiators being 'in series' (to use an electrical analogy), the cumulative resistance would be far beyond the capability of the pump.

Microbore systems do *not* require a special radiator. It is simply a matter of using adaptors to fit the smaller pipework.

Another aspect of the same question is that radiators, being mainly of steel construction, need the protection afforded by an indirect system to avoid massive corrosion or heavy scaling up.

What are convectors?

Convectors for wet systems contain a heat exchanger, usually a coil, which is hidden within a casing (Fig. 3.12). Natural convectors, i.e. those which depend upon nature to circulate their warm air product, use the casing as a kind of chimney, which channels rising air over the heat exchanger. The casing itself does not usually get very warm, hence there is almost no surface radiation from this device. Because of the low temperature, this type of convector is safe with very small

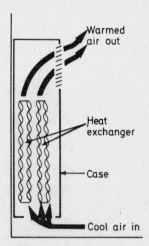

Figure 3.12   Principle of natural convector

children. Natural convectors, like radiators, must be situated where the rising current of warm air has freedom to move most widely. See Fig. 3.13.

Fan convectors, on the other hand, rely upon a fan to eject the warmed air, and as Fig. 3.14 shows it is customary to give the air a very different direction, downwards. From floor level, it can begin to rise as before. The great advantage of this is that it promotes a much better vertical temperature gradient, which is the difference between head and feet temperature. The natural convector, as will be understood from the sketch, is responsible for hot heads and cool feet.

The third type of appliance is the skirting heater, shown in Fig. 3.3. This has many advantages. It is unobtrusive, does not require wall space, and it is responsible for an excellent vertical temperature gradient, almost as good as the fan convector. In most models its output may be modified by use of a damper which can limit the amount of air passing over the heat

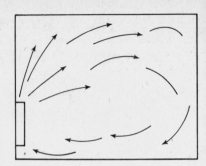

Figure 3.13   Convector air pattern (compare radiator, Figure 3.9)

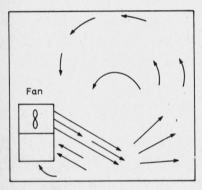

Fan

Figure 3.14   Air travel pattern from a fan convector

exchanger. It is selected by length, being made in modules each of a certain rated heat output averaging about 450 W/m or Btu/h.

Then why do skirting heaters not take over the market?

Principally, because they cost more. But it is also possible to run out of available wall, particularly if furniture, for example a sideboard, occupies part of one wall. They deserve serious consideration from anyone for whom price is not the first consideration.

What situations call for convectors instead of radiators?

As well as domestic premises, they are very well suited to museums, art galleries and the like, where an overall even temperature is the aim. Radiators, with their radiant output, tend to create warm zones as well as general warmth. At home the hall is well suited to a convector. So is a games room or a garage, or landing.

Another situation for convectors is that in which it would be unsuitable to have an area of warmth in front of the appliance; or where a relatively cool surface to the appliance is required. The nursery, a narrow study, these are examples of such a situation.

The convector is a safe appliance when a radiator is not, in cases where a high pressure circulating system is being used to promote high temperature water. A radiator surface would become dangerously hot to touch.

What special advantages do fan convectors have?

We have noted their ability, if correctly installed, to promote a vertical temperature gradient of only 2—3 deg C.

Their output is almost entirely governed by the fan. Consequently they are controllable on/off at the touch of a switch, or with even less trouble by a clock. In addition, they have an inbuilt room thermostat, and generally a speed control switch for quick warm-up and slower normal running (Figs. 3.15 and 3.16).

What situations suit fan convectors best?

Fan convectors belong in living rooms, where they can be switched on for a rapid warm-up, and kept in use for as long as the room is occupied, then switched off. Because the thermostat may give a slight but audible click, they are not recommended for bedrooms.

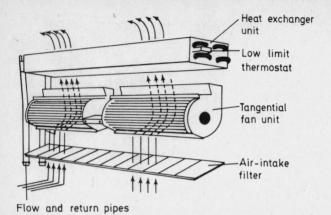

Figure 3.15 Principle of the fan convector (Myson)

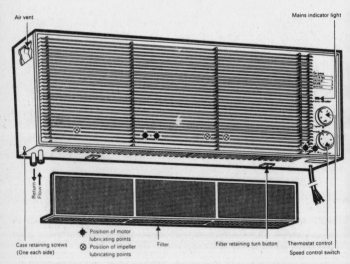

Figure 3.16 Typical fan convector with air filter removed (Myson)

Is a limited system more economical?

There are recognised categories, applicable to both wet and dry systems, and it is important to decide which you want.

Full central heating will provide simultaneously in all heated rooms the chosen design room temperature. It gives the maximum results for the greatest running cost.

Partial central heating will provide a simultaneous service as above, but to only a part of the house where you have chosen to have heat emitters.

Background central heating is a fully installed system which because of lower heating power can maintain a lower temperature, no more probably than about 15°C. The source of heat and the emitters are scaled down, making a cheaper installation. The intention is that specific areas, e.g. living room, will be brought up to full comfort temperature by another means, preferably a radiant source such as a gas fire.

Selective central heating has an installed system capable of giving a full service, but the heat source large enough only to satisfy a proportion of the system's needs. This proportion is chosen by the number of rooms likely to be occupied simultaneously. For most people this is the really sensible system, for we rarely occupy all rooms all the time. Having a smaller heat source (boiler etc) not only saves capital, but it also saves running cost because the heat source is likely to have a greater load factor, i.e. will work longer and so at greater efficiency. Yet it does not deny any part of the house the privilege of being warmed. The householder must turn room emitters on and off as required — which he should do in any case.

There are variants on the above, for example partial background, or selective background. The latter has much to recommend it. It has the virtues of a selective system, along with the possibility of using a radiant source for the final temperature. Recent investigations have shown just how valuable and effective radiant heat is. Selective background heating takes full advantage of that, and is recommended as the most economical system.

37

What is a design temperature?

The calculation which shows what size system a house needs is called the design. Taking each room separately, and assuming that the outdoor temperature is $-1\,^\circ$C, the heat loss is calculated bearing in mind the temperature which is required in that room. It is for the customer to nominate the required temperature, but there are common sense guidelines. The contractor is then under an obligation to supply and fit equipment which will maintain the required temperature, under the stated outdoor conditions.

The guidelines mentioned are given below. This is the time to warn that there is no advantage in taking too generous a view of the requirements. Having a 'bit in hand for emergencies' is counter-productive since it can lead only to the very common situation in which, for most of the time, the system is considerably larger than is needed. In consequence it works at lowered efficiency, at greater cost per heat unit.

	$^\circ$C	$^\circ$F
Living room	21–24	70–75
Dining Room	18–21	65–70
Bedrooms	cold to 18	cold to 65
Bathroom	18	65
Hall	16	60
Kichen, allowing for adventitious warming by cooker etc	18	65

Do the higher temperatures encourage drying of the air?

The relative humidity decreases as the temperature rises. It does so outdoors on a hot summer day, for example, but that does not send us scurrying for humidifiers. The only situations requiring artificial humidification are those where antique furniture and certain bronchial or sinus complaints are to be found. In the latter case reliance upon medical advice is recommended. If required, the cheaper forms of humidifier are usually adequate for the job.

By what rules do we choose a pump?

The only rule worth remembering is that you do not choose a small bore pump or circulator to fit into a microbore installation. For the rest, there is enough similarity in all but the largest domestic premises for one size of pump to cope with them all. There is a choice, of course, and it would be wise to delay ordering until the heating design calculation is complete. But the ordinary pump is large enough, and for smaller installations and for final adjustment of the system, the output is reduced. This may be done by means of an adjustment damper on the pump itself, or by closing the gate valve on the pump *outlet* until the required throughput is obtained. There should be gate valves on inlet and outlet, for ease of servicing.

What is the required output?

It is conveniently measured by the drop in temperature across the circuit when it is fully at work. We are looking for a difference in temperature between the water leaving and returning to the boiler of roughly 10 deg C (20 deg F). Increasing the flow rate decreases the differential and vice versa.

Working at that throughput the pump should not show any tendency to 'pump over', i.e. to discharge water from the overflow. If it does this it must be stopped at once by reducing the throughput and the reason sought. It may be that the pump will have to be transferred from the return to the flow pipe from the boiler, in order to diminish the effect of its discharge by the time it reaches the vent off take. We are still seeking to maintain the stated temperature difference across the circuit.

Would it be wise to choose a two speed pump?

Why? You have only one installation, and it is not an item which can be lent to a neighbour. Nor, in view of the present reliability of pumps, is there much justification for the twin pumps module, with one working and one standby.

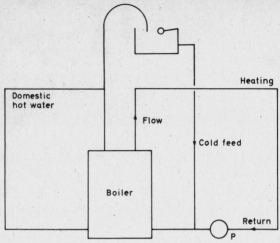

Figure 3.17   Pump in the return pipe

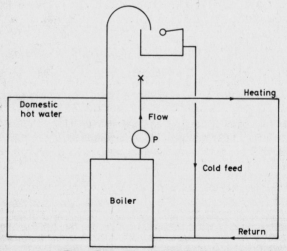

Figure 3.18   Pump in the flow pipe

40

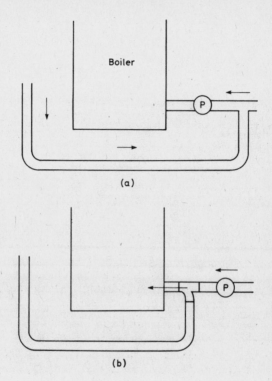

Figure 3.19 Natural circulation is prevented in (a) when the pump is not in use, but possible with the arrangement shown in (b)

How is the pump position, on flow or return, decided?

Again, we have the great domestic average. In most homes the vertical distance between the water in the feed/expansion cistern in the loft, and the highest point in the heating circuit, probably the top of a bedroom radiator, is at least 2½ m or 7–8 ft. This is greater than the pump 'head', and there is no danger of 'pumping over' the overflow. The pump may therefore be fitted in the heating return. That is why, in the gas boiler combination known as a small bore unit, which includes a pump and other auxiliary items, the pump is always connected to the return. See Fig. 3.17.

If the installation does not conform to the minimum dimension given then the pump must go on the flow side, as shown in Fig. 3.18. It must be noted that in practice the opposed returns shown in these two diagrams are not permissible unless the boiler is known to have an internal baffle which will prevent the one return flow from overpowering the other. In practice they are usually led in at the same side.

How are the two return pipes, from hot water and heating, combined?

Fig. 3.19 shows two ways of doing this. The first gives the domestic hot water return the advantage of pump suction — but only when the pump is at work. This situation does not offer any advantage in summer, since natural circulation will probably be stopped. The second method, using the pitcher tee as shown, does not inhibit natural circulation and also derives some benefit from the pump when at work.

Should the cold feed pipe be incorporated with the vent pipe?

It should not. This economy is practiced at times. But the two functions are of primary importance and are quite opposite in action. Each should have its own pipe.

4

BOILERS

Does the choice of boiler influence system design?

No. But in some circumstances the opposite is true. Take a 'heating only' system which, being small bore or microbore, is capable of being shut down instantaneously. You could not use a boiler incapable of following suit. This would debar the use of solid fuel or of one of the cruder high/low flame oil boilers which are probably not any longer made.

Both types of boiler would be suitable for the old fashioned gravity circuit heating with no on/off controls. But in practice they rely upon the incorporation of the domestic hot water function. By this means, the surplus heat available when a small or microbore system shuts down is channelled into the hot water cylinder, which has a large buffer capacity.

Are solid fuel boilers worth considering?

Any fuel which promises a 300 year future is worth considering. But there are other reasons for giving serious consideration to solid fuel. In late years, the choice has dwindled, for lack of public interest, difficulty in obtaining anthracite and so on. Only the back boiler market has thrived, and that very much down market, where the limited output from back boilers was such an improvement on conditions before. Back boiler units, it will be noted, did not have fuel supply problems because the research has been done which enables them to burn house coal and still conform to the Smoke Control orders.

Next please note that just about the best a back boiler will do, in practice, is 7.5 kW or 25 000 Btu/h. This is a figure which has represented for the average household enough heat to do a background or partial heating only. But now, if we all do our utmost with insulating; and if the low energy house becomes the new housing of the future; then 7.5 kW is going to be the new maximum, instead of, as at present, nearer to 15 kW.

So, serious students of home heating must stop dismissing the humble if ubiquitous coal back boiler with some contempt, and look again at the role which it can play in the nation's future comfort.

What are automatic boilers?

All gas fired and oil fired boilers are to a lesser or greater extent automatic. This means principally that they respond to a built-in thermostat, which regulates the fuel supply to the burner, to ensure that the hot water produced does not exceed a selected temperature. This is a great safety factor. By far the greater number of these boilers now have electric controls, and this permits the introduction of other switching devices, e.g. a clock, sometimes a room thermostat, a low level thermostat to guard against freezing during an 'off' period, and so on.

What is the choice among gas boilers?

There are three main lines: the commonest, the freestanding kitchen boiler, with or without enamelled case, which may be situated under the stairs, in the attic, anywhere subject to suiting the system; the back boiler, a great space saver since it takes no visible room but sits in the back of the hearth (Fig. 4.1); and the wall hung boiler, which takes no floor space. Some models of the last type employ an advanced technology in order to combine high output with low water content, in safety. Others are elevated models of the now conventional type.

Choice is not concerned with merit but with what suits the house and the system. Notably there is the space taken,

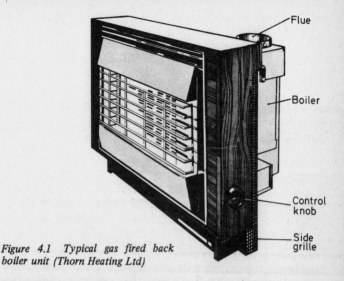

Flue

Boiler

Control knob

Side grille

Figure 4.1 Typical gas fired back boiler unit (Thorn Heating Ltd)

mentioned in the last paragraph. In the higher output range the freestanding boiler is the only contender. Also choice should be restricted to boilers which have British Gas approval.

Can a back boiler be fitted to an existing gas fire?

No. Although gas fire/back boiler units are rightly advertised as acting independently on either fire or boiler, the whole appliance is a very carefully designed integration. Among other things the two parts have a common gas inlet, common flue and central control. Though the manufacturer of the combination may not be the maker of the fire, he modifies standard fires to suit his special needs. Only the manufacturer can do this.

Will a gas fired back boiler fit into any hearth?

It will fit any hearth opening which is of standard dimensions. This may eliminate some older ones, but most post war

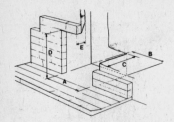

	min		max	
	mm	in	mm	in
A	406	16	550	21
B	579	22¾		
C	343	13½		
D	542	21⅜	560	22
E			165	6½

Figure 4.2 Standard fireplace stripped to brickwork (Thorn Heating Ltd)

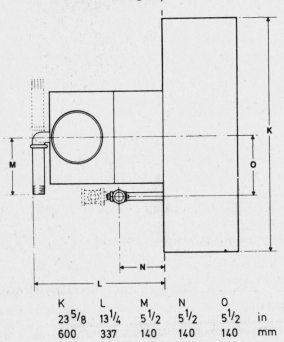

K	L	M	N	O	
23⅝	13¼	5½	5½	5½	in
600	337	140	140	140	mm

Figure 4.3 Plan view of typical gas fired back boiler unit (Thorn Heating Ltd)

housing will conform. A standard opening, with cheeks and decoration removed, i.e. down to brickwork, is about 550 mm (21½ in) high; 406–550 mm (16–21 in) wide; and 343 mm (13½ in) deep (Figs 4.2 and 4.3).

How much wall does a wall hung boiler need?

Manufacturers make great efforts to bring any kitchen fitted boiler into line with other kitchen fitment dimensions. In the case of wall hung boilers, the principal target is back-to-front depth to match kitchen cabinets. The boiler illustrated (Fig. 4.4)

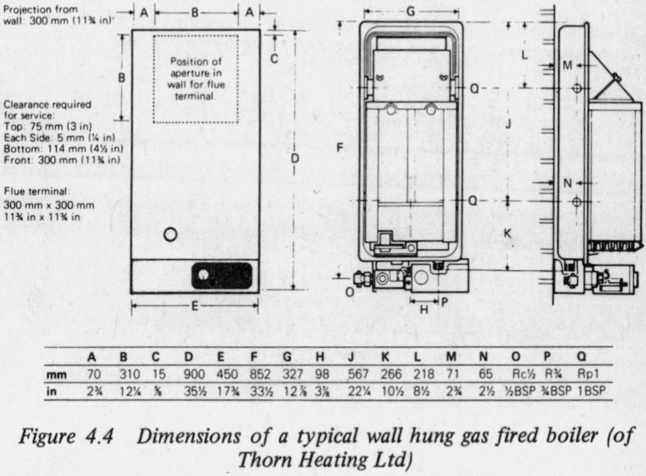

	A	B	C	D	E	F	G	H	J	K	L	M	N	O	P	Q
mm	70	310	15	900	450	852	327	98	567	266	218	71	65	Rc½	R¾	Rp1
in	2¾	12¼	⅝	35½	17¾	33½	12⅞	3⅞	22¼	10½	8½	2¾	2½	½BSP	¾BSP	1BSP

Figure 4.4 Dimensions of a typical wall hung gas fired boiler (of Thorn Heating Ltd)

has achieved this target of 300 mm (11¾ in). Its other principal statistics are: wall occupied, height 900 mm (35½ in) width 450 mm (17¾ in): water content 4.5 lit (1 gal) for the larger size boiler: weight (also for the larger boiler) 62 kg (136 lb). These data relate to the Thorn Olympic boiler, which is cast iron. The illustration shows the dimensions in detail.

Does the weight make fitting a problem?

If the fixing devices are correctly attached to a permanent wall (not to a light partition) then the weight is no problem. Failure is rarely caused by bad walls, generally by bad fixing. A further easement, which could make fixing a one-man job, lies in the fact that what is secured to the wall is a relatively light

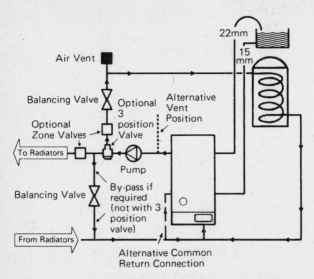

Figure 4.5 Fully pumped systems for use with thermostatic radiator valves or zone valves or 3 position valve (Thorn Heating Ltd)

weight mounting plate. The only time the boiler has to be lifted is when it is hung on the mounting plate. There is no difference in weight or overall dimensions between the conventional and balanced flue models.

Figs. 4.5, 4.6 and 4.7 show the maker's recommendation for connecting the boiler into different types of circuit.

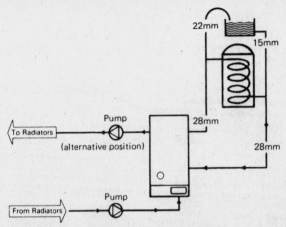

Figure 4.6   Gravity hot water with pumped heating. The heating return MUST be connected to ¾ in. BSP male connection under the boiler (Thorn Heating Ltd)

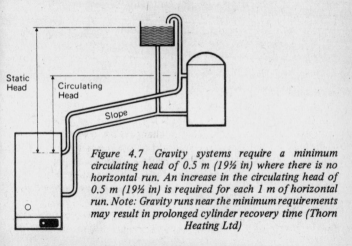

Figure 4.7   Gravity systems require a minimum circulating head of 0.5 m (19½ in) where there is no horizontal run. An increase in the circulating head of 0.5 m (19½ in) is required for each 1 m of horizontal run. Note: Gravity runs near the minimum requirements may result in prolonged cylinder recovery time (Thorn Heating Ltd)

How important is British Gas approval?

It is the only assurance a buyer can get that the boiler has been designed and constructed to modern sound principles, for safety and efficiency of operation. The Gas Safety Regulations 1972 took the somewhat advanced step of making the householder personally responsible for the safety of the gas system and appliances on his property. This applies even though a contractor may have been employed. British Gas will give every assistance in seeing that things are made and kept safe. But they will expect that the principal item has passed their own stringent tests.

What is a range rated boiler?

This is one boiler, structurally, which is capable of being set to one of two or more maximum output rates. This enables a manufacturer to offer a wider choice to the public, without the cost which would be involved in producing two or three different units. There are other advantages. For instance, a boiler set to the lower of its ratings may be adequate for the system as installed, but if an extra radiator or two are added later, the boiler rating can be increased to take care of the added load. All boilers which are capable of being range rated are clearly described in the maker's specification.

Why cannot every boiler be range rated?

Any boiler can have its maximum output altered. It is just a matter of changing the operating gas pressure, or the size of burner orifice, or both. But that is not range rating. The almost certain result of making random changes of the sort noted will be a loss of efficiency, perhaps right across the range.

Those boilers which are designated range rated have come from the development laboratories of the manufacturer after usually long trials, and have then been examined by British Gas testing laboratories. The essential feature of range rating is that at all the ratings specified, achieved by the precise means instructed by the makers, a boiler will perform at its peak efficiency. It must be added that the means and the information needed to change from one rating to another are not available to the public. It is a skilled job.

Are gas boilers difficult to install and maintain?

The answer is a qualified 'No'. An important part of British Gas approval is that each appliance shall be accompanied by instructions which have also to pass the test of completeness and comprehensibility. But they are judged at professional level. To understand them fully you need to, as it were, speak the language — to do as instructed by knowing what the instruction means. Within those limits the way is made plain, in both installation and maintenance.

Do gas boilers have to be joined to a chimney?

There are two versions of most gas boilers, those made for conventional flue, i.e. a chimney or similar, and those made for balanced flue (or similar). The latter are known as room sealed appliances. The balance of a balanced flue is achieved by letting the flue gases out by a part of the same device which allows the combustion air to enter.

Conventional models do have to be joined physically into a chimney or flue pipe. It is increasingly common, and very good practice, to join them to a flue pipe, called a liner, which runs inside a chimney and reduces its effective cross sectional area (Fig. 4.8). This avoids any chimney defects, and gives greater velocity to the issuing gases, thus overcoming any resistance in the chimney. The down draught diverter, which is necessary for bypassing any down draughts which would otherwise affect combustion, is made as an integral part of the boiler (Fig. 4.9).

Can an independent flue pipe be used?

In cases where there is no suitable chimney a conventionally flued boiler may very well be connected to a flue pipe. There

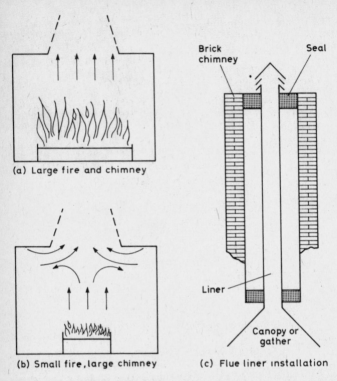

(a) Large fire and chimney

(b) Small fire, large chimney

Brick chimney

Seal

Liner

Canopy or gather

(c) Flue liner installation

Figure 4.8 The chimney must be efficient and properly sized for its job. With a small fire and a large chimney this can be achieved by using a flue liner and a canopy or 'gather'

are two main conditions. It should not promote excessive cooling of the flue gases, which would lead to condensation and internal corrosion, and it must terminate in a down draught free area, with an approved type of terminal fitted.

The first condition may be satisfied in more than one way. Subject to satisfying the Building Regulations, notably over

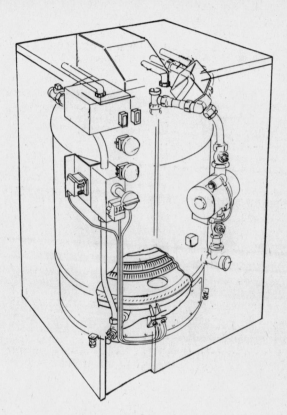

Figure 4.9   The Worcester Delglo boiler, with incorporated hot water cylinder (Delta)

fire risks, such a flue pipe may be run mainly indoors, to avoid overcooling. In so doing it can contribute a little towards house warming. If run outdoors, it will be, preferably, of asbestos, and should be coated with an insulating material covered by a weatherproof jacket. To avoid that much trouble it is preferable simply to use a double walled asbestos pipe. The size, generally 100 m or 4 in for the lower ranges of boilers and 125 mm or 5 in for the medium range, is specified in the installation instructions already mentioned.

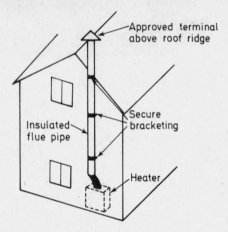

Figure 4.10   External flue pipe bracketed to gable end

The second condition will be satisfied in most cases if the terminal is about 0.6 m or 2 ft above house ridge level. Taller buildings or trees in the vicinity could affect this, and if in doubt consult the gas people. The problem of supporting the length of flue is readily solved by running it up a gable end, where it can be bracketed all the way (Fig. 4.10).

What if there is no chimney, and a flue pipe is not welcome?

This is where the balanced flue appliance comes in. Indeed, in the view of part of the gas industry, the balanced flue is now first choice. Our view still is that if you have a good chimney you should use it, not least because the appliance costs less.

However, it is there as a valid choice (Fig. 4.11). The two parts of a balanced flue may be concentric (Fig. 4.12), or divided with flue gas outlet above air inlet. This is immaterial and unalterable since the manufacturer decides, and the equipment is a part of the unit.

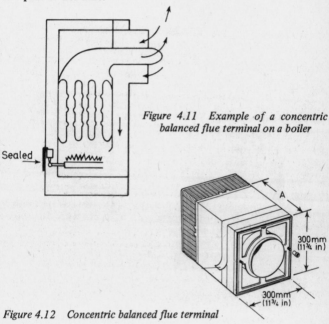

Figure 4.11   Example of a concentric balanced flue terminal on a boiler

Figure 4.12   Concentric balanced flue terminal

There are a few simple rules about fitting. The terminal must not be near a door or openable window, through which flue products could re-enter the house. It must not discharge at low level into a public right of way, and in any case must be protected by a grille to avoid becoming a receptacle for unwanted objects e.g. from small boys. It should not be near enough to, say, a fence or bush which would deflect the wind into eddy currents.

Technically, it is set so that the flue gas outlet projects an inch or so beyond the wall surface. The aperture through the wall may be weather faced with cement rendering on the outside, but it is usual to allow for some thermal movement by filling the annulus between wall and terminal with insulating packing.

It is desirable to study the Building Regulations, as well as makers' instructions, before fitting a balanced flue terminal.

Can a chimney be added to a chimneyless house?

Yes. It is relatively easy to add a chimney to an existing house, and the result can be quite attractive. This however is not an easy job for the householder. Properly constructed chimneys are made from precast blocks, each correctly shaped for its position in the finished job.

Is gas boiler position influenced by anything but its flue?

A gas boiler requires free area in front of it, of its own back-to-front depth, to allow for removal of the burner when servicing. That is the only serious condition. Otherwise, no matter how confined the space, wall insulation and ample ventilation can be arranged. As a result, the under-stairs space is often used.

What is ample ventilation?

This matter has been laid down by British Gas, and details may be obtained from the local showroom. The principal conditions are:

Air for combustion of a conventionally flued appliance must have permanent free access to the boiler, from an adjacent room to the room in which the boiler is situated, through an opening or grille of free area equal to 6.5 cm^2 per 0.29 kW (or 1 in^2 per 1 000 Btu/h). If the opening or grille leads direct to outdoors, half that area is sufficient. The adjacent room must itself be able to obtain a free supply of air. The opening into the boiler room must be at low level. At high level there must be a similar opening, half the area, for the escape of warmed air, to prevent a local temperature build-up.

Room sealed appliances do not need combustion air. They need the same high level vent, and to admit the air which will be warmed, a low level vent of the same area.

It is wise to check the details with the gas people. Another matter in which their advice is needed concerns those cases in which an extraction fan is at work in the same room as the boiler, as can easily happen in a kitchen. The inlet vent sizes given above will not then be adequate, since the fan has an appetite for air itself. Deciding what is adequate is best left to a trained man.

What lights a gas boiler?

In most cases we are really talking of two stages of lighting. Most boilers operate by means of a permanent pilot light. So it is a pilot which lights the main burner whenever the boiler

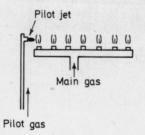

Figure 4.13   Simple pilot ignition

thermostat 'calls for heat' (Fig. 4.13). Please note that the pilot jet and the burner – and indeed the boiler – are a matched set. You cannot fit any pilot you choose. The other stage of lighting concerns how the pilot is lit. In conventionally flued appliances this may be manual, by a match or taper. Or, now less commonly, it may be by glow coil heated by mains

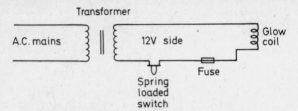

Figure 4.14   Filament igniter from mains supply

electricity which has been transformed, usually to 12 V (Fig.
4.14). The coils burn out fairly frequently. There is no doubt
that the most used method now is piezo-electric. A trigger
mechanism causes a small hammer to hit a crystal and generate
a spark of about 10 000 V.

All these methods but the manual one can be used with
room sealed appliances.

A complaint about pilot ignition is that in the course of a
year the pilot burns a surprising amount of gas. The alternative,
usually called magneto ignition, avoids a pilot by having a
mains generated spark struck by the action of the thermostat
(or clock) which energises the boiler at the start of an 'on' period.
Results so far have not lived up to the expectations, and the
pilot remains the usual method.

How does a boiler 'fail safe'?

It is one of the blessings of a pilot controlled burner that the
pilot also operates the fail-safe, the electro-magnetic valve
which holds open the main gas way. Consequently, if the pilot
flame, which is needed to light the main burner, goes out, gas
cannot flow to the main burner, and unlit gas cannot
accumulate. A rare failure of the thermocouple itself leaves the
burner shut off. During first lighting, i.e. when lighting the
pilot, a supply of gas to the pilot burner has to be obtained by
manually holding open the gas valve, for a period of 30–40
seconds until the thermocouple takes charge.

What controls does a gas boiler need?

There are essential controls, the boiler thermostat and the multifunctional control (Fig. 4.15). The latter is so called because it performs several functions. It houses the main gas inlet and outlet, pilot outlet, thermocouple terminal, governor, main gas valve and spring loaded manual valve opener — see last question. The boiler thermostat connects into it. These days it is rarely anything but electrical in operation. This means that any device capable of switching, e.g. a clock or another thermostat, can be used to control operation simply by being wired in series into the circuit.

Many boilers doing a job of heating plus domestic hot water also have a programmer fitted, but this is not essential.

Is it more economical to keep the boiler thermostat low?

Not necessarily. There is a point, about 60°C or 140°F, below which you should not go. It encourages internal condensation

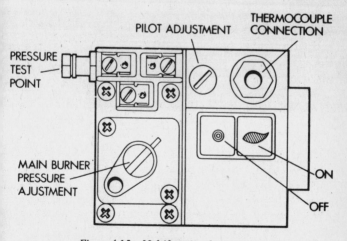

Figure 4.15   Multifunctional gas control

in the flueways, and this leads to corrosion of the boiler. So much for the theory that a boiler wears out less quickly if kept cool!

The real economy in boiler running comes from continuous working, the avoidance of those long periods of rest between spells of work which allow a lot of heat to dissipate uselessly, only to need replacing at the next 'on' period. (It is also the convincing case against oversizing the boiler, even to the extent of deliberately adding 10 or 15% margin above the calculated requirement.) The user can do a lot to help himself in this matter. Take, for instance, heating throughout the season. There may come a time in mid-winter when the heating seems inadequate. That is the time to turn up the thermostat, perhaps to 90°C to 190°F. But if it is left there, the time will come when the boiler is shutting off for perhaps 40 minutes in each hour. Reducing the thermostat is clearly going to improve that, and you may safely reduce to about 70°C or 160°F. If the boiler does not shut off at all you have overdone it, and must set it up a little.

What does a programmer do?

A programmer is just a complex switching device with a clock built in (Fig. 4.16). Programmers give a choice of operating programmes ranging from continuous shut-down or off to continuous working of both heating and hot water. The area in between is divided between various combinations of hot water on and off and heating and hot water on and off. The times of on and off are arranged on the clock by setting the 'tappets' around the perimeter. These usually allow for two on and off periods in 24 hours, the minimum time between changes being about ¾ hour.

In a system of pumped heating and gravity hot water, the latter cannot be stopped while heating proceeds, but the reverse is true. This is rarely a disadvantage, for once the hot water is at the temperature required no further heat will be consumed on that circuit despite the on position. When setting a clock,

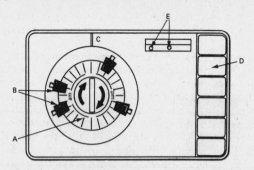

A 24-hour clock (read against mark C).
B Movable 'on' and 'off' switches act as they pass C.
D Push-button switches set the full range of combinations of 'constant', 'timed' and 'off' for space heating and water heating.
E Indicator lights show when space heating and water heating are operating.

Figure 4.16   A typical modern programmer

in a programmer or not, note that it has Day and Night zones, and also a setting point so that it may be put to the right time.

Is it advantageous to have a lot of programmes?

Not if cost is important. In our experience even those people who have paid for a complex programmer with 10 or more programmes rarely use more than 3 or 4.

What would a typical programmer setting look like?

Let us take a typical family in which both parents go out to work and the children go to school. For 5 days a week in winter we might have:

06.30   Boiler comes on, with dhw (domestic hot water) and heating.

61

07.30	Family get up, to warmed house and ample hot water.
08.30	Last of family leaves home, boiler shuts down.
16.00 (or 16.30)	Boiler comes on, with heating and dhw.
17.00	First of family reach a ready warmed home.
20.00 to 21.00	Ample hot water for baths.
23.00	Last of family goes to bed. Boiler shuts down.

The times may well vary in any given case, but the reasoning is clear. At weekends we may find either extreme, of a family at home all day, or of a family out all day, or even out for the weekend.

Should heating be left on if the house is empty for days?

With so much to lose it can be a good insurance to leave the heating in an on position: the boiler thermostat low: and the programmer set to come on for about 3 hours during the estimated coldest parts of the day. One of these may be taken to be the small hours, the other preferably at the other side of the clock, i.e. (say) on at 02.00 and 14.00. There is however another way to do it, more economically. This is to employ a low limit thermostat, often called a frost stat. The sensor of this has to be situated in what is deemed to be the most critical place, where freezing would occur first. An obvious place would be beside a boiler if this were fitted in an outhouse. Indoors, it might be by the feed expansion cistern in the loft. A frost stat is usually set to react when it senses a temperature down to about $5-6°C$. Its reaction is to bring the boiler on, until the ambient temperature has improved enough to cause it to cancel its reaction.

The important thing about such a thermostat, and one to be checked very carefully, is that it is correctly wired in. For it is required to override all other boiler controls except the boiler thermostat. Everything else will be set at off but a frost stat correctly wired will nevertheless bring the boiler on.

How do oil fired boilers compare with gas boilers?

They have similarities, for example in being fully automatic and therefore suited to work with rapid acting controls, e.g. in a 'heating only' circuit. They can be controlled by a wide range of controllers, because they are with few exceptions electrically controlled themselves. They have the same needs for combustion air and ventilation, the same demand for an efficient flue or chimney.

Among the differences: two grades of fuel, known as gas oil, class D, and domestic oil, class C, and by other names. The first is now generally accepted as suited to outhouse boilers only, the other being for indoor use. Then there are specific types of boilers, first pressure jet, with a gun-like burner (Fig. 4.18). While present day advertising is often directed to saying how quiet they are, this is because they have always been noted for noise, and better fitted in an outhouse than indoors. Seek proof of quiet running if choosing one for indoors. There are two types of vaporising burner, one known as the wall flame, the other, generally, as the pot type (Fig. 4.17). Potential noise apart, choice may be further restricted by availability. Pressure jets have never been made in the small sizes which should be the target of every energy and cost conscious householder in the smaller home. The overall choice is not likely to increase now, unless it be in the desired downward direction of rating.

Warning: make sure that you can get a continuing supply of oil locally, as a new customer, before proceeding.

How big an oil storage tank do I need?

As big as you can, to take advantage of bulk delivery discounts and provide the maximum buffer stock against emergencies. And as small as you can, because it is an unsightly addition to the garden, best hidden behind trees but easily rusted by the water dripping from trees.

A compromise, then, and one which you would best resolve by having a chat with the dealer whom you hope will be supplying the oil. Special factors apart there is a sort of formula in existence for arriving at tank size.

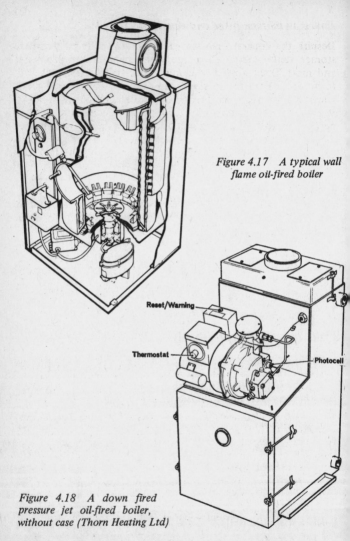

*Figure 4.17   A typical wall
flame oil-fired boiler*

Reset/Warning

Thermostat

Photocell

*Figure 4.18   A down fired
pressure jet oil-fired boiler,
without case (Thorn Heating Ltd)*

How is an oil tank fitted and equipped?

Despite the apparent advantages it is rare to find a domestic storage tank buried. There are great maintenance problems, and most likely a need to employ suction to retrieve the oil. It is after all better to stand the tank on short brick piers, where gravity feeds the fuel to the boiler and where it can be inspected and painted. Fig. 4.19 shows the method of connection in both cases, the suction system being known as a 2-pipe system because oil not needed by the burner returns to the tank by a second pipe. It will be seen that the tank

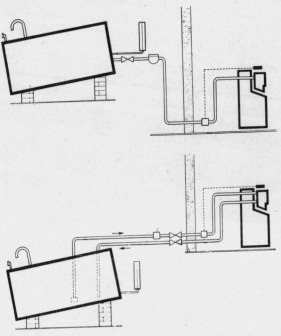

Figure 4.19   Single-pipe and two-pipe oil supply system to a pressure system jet boiler

slopes towards the sludge cock end, and is equipped with sight glass, filler cap and vent pipe. The provision of a fire valve is now generally compulsory. The sensor should be above the boiler. Another technical requirement is a micronic filter, preferably situated out of doors, in the feed line. This must, of course, be inspected and cleaned regularly.

How does a pressure jet burner work?

The gun type burner (Figs. 4.20 and 4.21) is fed with pressurised oil and air, the proportions being carefully adjusted, i.e. the amount of oil fired is set by the size of the nozzle, and the air shutters are adjusted to suit that flow. Then, when the thermostat calls for heat, a spark is generated across the end of the nozzle, and oil mist/air mixture emerges and is lit (Fig. 4.22). This process can go on only as long as a light-sensitive cell in the burner control box can 'see' that there is a

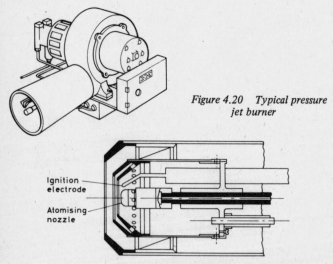

Figure 4.20   Typical pressure jet burner

Ignition electrode

Atomising nozzle

Figure 4.21   A typical combustion head used in a pressure jet burner

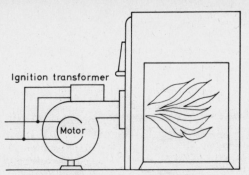

Figure 4.22   How a pressure jet burner fires

flame. If it sees no flame, the operation stops. (Compare the thermocouple in gas boilers.) But it will, first time, assume an error, and try to begin the lighting procedure from the start. Only after that fails will it give up and 'go to lockout', at which point human intervention is needed. Many such cases indicate nothing worse than a coating of soot on the glass window through which the selenium cell 'sees' the flame. Clean this and everything works again.

Is sooting a problem?

It is fair to say that oil burners soot more readily than gas burners do, since oil has more complex hydrocarbons. Equal care is needed with both oil and gas to get the best and most efficient air mixture, but the consequences of failure are usually more apparent with oil. Maintenance of oil fired appliances always includes cleaning soot from burner, heat exchanger and generally from the flue. It should not, however, be regarded as a special problem, more a way of life where oil is used. Solid fuel is a soot producer too.

Is oil used in anything other than boilers?

There are free standing paraffin stoves, which are flueless and produce a gallon of water for every gallon of paraffin burned.

Even though these are now safely self-extinguishing, they should be avoided if possible, being instruments of condensation. The fixed flued radiator-convector (Fig. 5.3) is another matter. Though the pressure has gone out of selling them, they are in the main a surprisingly effective way of producing enough heat for most of the house, at a very low (comparatively) installed cost. They are mainly hearth fitting, and their entire output of warmed air is generated at the hearth. Unlike more expensive systems, the air has to find its own way around the house. This will happen moderately well if all doors are left open, or it can be helped by fitting an extraction fan high up in the wall of the room, to push warmed air out into the hall, stairway or wherever suits the house layout.

There is also a limited number of oil fired ducted warm air units on the market, too.

Do oil fired units need skilled servicing?

Yes. The simpler types of unit such as the hearth convector do not demand special knowledge. But a complex automatic mechanism, such as the pressure jet, must be serviced with the same degree of knowledge which you would expect a modern car to get, with due regard for precise measurements of gaps, nozzle projection and so on. Servicing must be done correctly.

Are solid fuel boilers similar to gas and oil fired boilers?

They look alike (Fig. 4.23) and they operate in the same range of heat outputs. But, it must be stressed that there is no such thing as 'gas central heating' or 'oil central heating' when referring to wet systems. A wet system is allied to the house, not to the boiler, and with certain limitations it does not matter what type of boiler fires it. This means that in a given system all boilers of the correct output are interchangeable (with certain limitations, mainly caused by the non-automatic response of solid fuel).

There are, however, many dissimilarities. Solid fuel (s.f.) boilers are intermittent in operation. Hopper fed boilers will

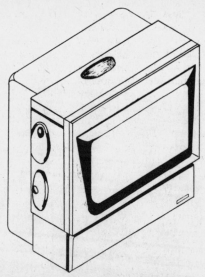

Figure 4.23   Room heater with back boiler

carry on at a steady rate but they must be fed, and cleaned out, at intervals rarely greater than 24 hours. Non-hopper types need more frequent attention, and the output has peaks and dips. It is often held against solid fuel that it entails labour, fetching fuel, removing ash, and so on. Don't forget, however, that our grandparents took this to be a part of domestic life. In the comparison, s.f. boilers are a blunt instrument. They have a boiler thermostat, but it cannot cleanly shut the boiler down. It reduces the air supply, and the fire, hence the output, gradually diminishes.

Can s.f. boilers be used safely in modern systems?

Certainly they can, in the majority of cases. For the reason given in the last answer, they cannot be used in systems which can shut down completely at a moments notice. Such a system would be one of heating only (no domestic hot water) controlled by any automatic means — roomstat, pump, clock, radstats. This type of system is not what we usually find, and it is quite safe to use s.f. boilers in a heating system controlled in this way, so long as there is a hot water cylinder in circuit, without any controls between it and the boiler.

Can s.f. boilers be made automatic in operation?

In the changed fuel circumstances, we may expect a resurgence of popularity of s,f. boilers, with a corresponding increase in

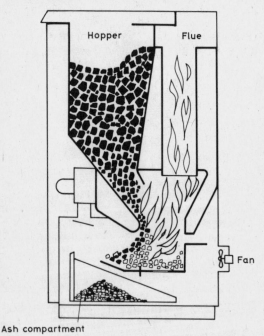

Figure 4.24 Gravity feed boiler with hopper and forced air

70

inventiveness among manufacturers. If this occurs almost anything is possible. At present the only thing approaching automatic working is a screw feeder, a cumbersome and expensive device for a larger domestic boiler, which requires a boiler house to accommodate it. Fan powered air supply increases controllability (Fig. 4.24).

Does the choice of type of solid fuel make any difference?

It can make a great deal of difference. We could begin by mentioning size. Makers of better class s.f. boilers specify the size grading of fuel to be used, and this is important, being associated with air travel through the fire bed, for example.

House coal is not a good fuel. This generates a lot of smoke and soot which clogs the heat exchanger and results in an early decrease in efficiency. It is likely that the research workers will find a way around this trouble, as they have done with room heaters. But the criteria are not quite the same in this case, and we must wait.

The range of choice is roughly bounded by (a) anthracite (b) Welsh steam coal, also called dry steam coal, Welsh nuts and other combinations, and (c) prepared fuels such as Coalite and briquettes. The leading choice is anthracite, as pure a fuel as you can get, usually with no more than 3% ash. Welsh steam is a good substitute, with more ash but almost smokeless and cheaper. Prepared fuels made from powdered coal should be examined in use to see whether they have a tendency towards ash masking, i.e. being covered by a thin film of ash during burning. If so they must be agitated occasionally, using the poker. Careful selection of feed stock has reduced this tendency.

Wood is entirely unsuited for use in a boiler not designed specifically for it.

The ultimate choice of fuel may, in the end, depend upon local availability, i.e. can you get regular and reliable supplies?

Where does the combination cooker with boiler fit into the pattern?

It is really in a class by itself, quite expensive though the cost includes assembly at site. It is an extremely efficient appliance, with a high capacity for storing heat and since it will do everything but grill it cannot be bettered as a single unit. That is by the way, and of special interest to those who live in country cottages. The combination cooker may be supplied with or without boiler, and it is important when purchasing to find out what the maximum boiler output is. In some models it is no more than 3 kW or 10 000 Btu/h, enough to supply domestic hot water. Other models are fitted with a larger boiler, and usually a means of diverting more or less heat from the furnace to either boiler or cooker section. Only the last type can be compared to domestic boilers in relation to heating circuits.

It is often claimed that s.f. back boilers will supply central heating. Will they?

It is right to doubt any statement quite so general. In the ordinary or average house at this time, the back boiler of a solid fuel room heater (Figs. 4.25 and 4.26) will supply partial heating, i.e. ample heat to a few radiators, or background heating, i.e. some heat to a greater number of radiators. Only in the smallest house could it claim to supply a full heating system. As indicated elsewhere, for energy conservation reasons, the target should now be so to reduce the heat demand of every house that a full system would be obtainable from a low output boiler, such as these are.

Are s.f. back boilers controllable?

An appliance of this kind has two parts. The front part is the fire, which may be of the open type, or closeable. Unlike the gas fired back boiler unit, boiler and fire are not independent. The fire must be at work. From that point, the manufacturer's literature will be found to give two sets of figures. One set shows the rated output from the fire at the front and the boiler at the back, when the damper is open. The other set shows both figures when the damper is closed. The totals in both cases are roughly equal, and it amounts to this, that you

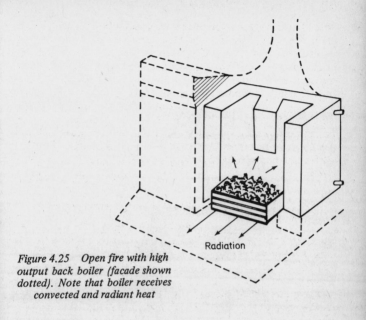

Figure 4.25 Open fire with high output back boiler (facade shown dotted). Note that boiler receives convected and radiant heat

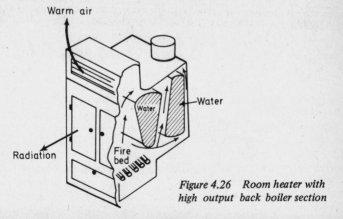

Figure 4.26 Room heater with high output back boiler section

73

choose at any one time whether to have more heat into the room or into the water.

A measure of control, but very imprecise, may be exercised by the size of the firebed. A high fire encourages a higher internal temperature.

What is rated output? Is it realistic?

The rated output is the output which has been achieved under standard test conditions. The tests themselves, and the conditions, are realistic. So long as an appliance is correctly maintained, the rated output may be obtained in use. But it must be added that the refined fuels give the more realistic results. Properly maintained gas and oil fired boilers will deliver their rated output without any coercion on the part of the user. It is their standard procedure. Solid fuel boilers, on the other hand, and in particular those of the non-hopper type, have to be carefully tended, in having the right grade of fuel and being tested at a certain stage in the 'life' of a charge of fuel. Their output will fall as the fire burns down, and after recharging when the radiant heat is masked from the heat exchanger, and if cold air is admitted during clinkering.

Hopper type s.f. boilers are very much more consistent, since there is no charging period and no burning down of the fire bed.

What allowances should be made for a cycling output from a s.f. boiler?

When a heat balance is drawn up for a house, the total heat loss represents the heat to be replaced by the boiler or other heat source. In practice, an allowance is added to this total when deciding the size of boiler to install. Originally the allowance was around 10%. But as time went on it came to be anything from 10% to 30%, and to adopt the role of being a safeguard against any errors likely to undersize the system.

It is quite wrong to apply it to gas and oil fired systems, and any allowance should not exceed 10% in s.f. systems.

Is it better to feed a non-hopper type boiler often, or at longer intervals?

So long as the job is done quickly, limiting the admission of cold air, frequent feeding is better because it avoids periods when the fire reaches a very low point and is then swamped with cold fuel.

Is it harmful for a boiler to sing?

This is known in the trade as kettling, because kettles do it. It is not in itself harmful, but is indicative of one of two things. The root cause is local boiling, the noise being the implosion of steam bubbles as they meet the main body of water and collapse.

The local boiling may be due to a thin coating of scale on the inside surface of the boiler. If water gets behind this, and becomes overheated, it will turn to steam and escape. So boiling may indicate that scale has formed inside the boiler, which is bound to have an effect upon heat exchange.

The other possible cause of local boiling is that a small area of the heat exchange surface receives heat at greater than the average rate. This could be caused by the casting being thin at certain points, or by irregularity in the heat application.

If kettling occurs in a boiler connected to a direct system it may be expected. But if the system is indirect, something may have gone wrong and it should be looked at.

What could go wrong with an indirect system to allow scale in the boiler?

The obvious thing is that the system is not in reality indirect, i.e. something is happening to bypass the system. A detailed analysis requires an expert on site, but as a general rule, the probable cause is something which destroys the closed nature of the system, so that instead of the same water circulating continuously for weeks and months on end, fresh supplies of raw water are finding their way into the primary system. This can only occur if water is lost from circulation. The job, then, is to find where? Through too frequent draining down? Through leakage? By being pumped over an overflow which does not return to the feed/expansion cistern? These are the most common causes.

What can be done if water is pumped over the overflow?

It is proof that the pump is working too strongly for the installation. The output must be reduced, by means of the adjustment if there is one, or by throttling a gate valve on the *outlet* side if not. Even if the overflow is returning to the feed/ expansion cistern it must be stopped. This leads to aeration of the water, a prime cause of internal corrosion.

5

DRY SYSTEMS

How would I choose a dry system suited to my needs?

As with all systems it depends upon your needs, and the first step is always to decide these, as far as is possible. What is important to you: cost of installation or running or both; continuous or intermittent use; landlord's property; approaching retirement; degree of occupancy of the house and so on.

Suppose I want the best, irrespective of cost, and equivalent to full central heating?

Then you should try very hard to accommodate a full ducted system, despite our own assertion that it is rarely suited to existing premises. There are ways of 'losing' ductwork, by choosing flat duct shapes, running ducts under floors and in lofts, exercising a free choice between having the outlets (the registers) in the floor or ceiling or side walls.

How would I design a full ducted system?

The basis of *all* heating systems is the heat balance, the initial calculation which shows how much heat will be lost from each room. This is dealt with in Chapter 9. From this we get the fundamental information, from size of heat generator to performance size of warm air outlets.

The detail then differs from that for wet systems. Air velocities, for instance, tend to be more critical than water velocities, and step reduction of duct area is not uncommon (Fig. 5.1).

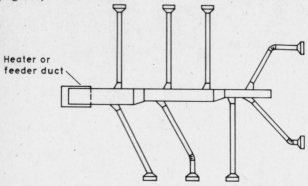

Heater or feeder duct

Figure 5.1   The stepped duct system. This may be in the elementary form shown, with only one main duct, or the heater may supply more than one main duct and, up to the capacity of the heater, form a radial system

Warm air design is not a very suitable field for the untrained man, however intelligent. But every one interested in the subject could get some benefit from reading a book compiled by those most concerned, the warm air specialists in the Society of British Gas Industries. This is the *Warm Air Design Manual* (Ernest Benn, 1976).

Would a stub duct system be more realistic for me?

It would be far easier, and a good deal cheaper, and in an existing house would avoid most of the snags mentioned several times. It would, of course, suffer somewhat in performance, since it delivers warm air to a small number of points for general distribution, instead of making specific deliveries to all chosen parts.

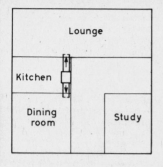

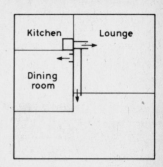

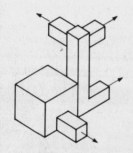

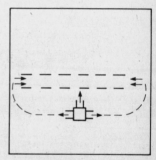

Figure 5.2   Typical stub duct layouts for different house plans. The diagram bottom left shows a stub duct system on two floors, while the bottom right diagram illustrates the idea of influencing air travel from a stub duct system by means of the return air duct

This means that the positions chosen for discharge must be chosen with as much care as circumstances permit. For example, to provide warm air for the first floor, discharge into the hall near the foot of the stairs is an obvious choice. Fig. 5.2 shows how a stub duct system may be made to conform to various indoor plans.

A further possible benefit of the stub duct system is that duct sizing is of no great significance. In general, the ducts may be of the size of the outlet from the heater, with terminal dampers so that the air flow may be varied, even pushed all in one direction for quick warming of one area. The use of thermostatically operated dampers, on this and on full duct systems, is to be encouraged.

Suppose I do not want any ducting at all?

The choice then opens out, from the crudest form of air heating, by a single appliance, to an aggregation of individual heaters often capable of close control. The first of these is a single heat generator, such as ducted systems have, but no ducts at all. It used to be typified by a unit called a 'brick central', but

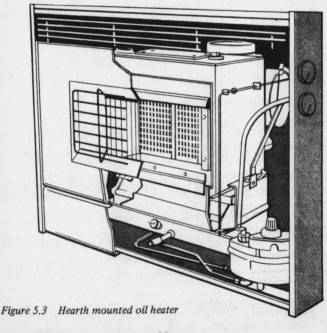

Figure 5.3   Hearth mounted oil heater

this massive structure is no longer sold. The current unit type is a hearth mounted apparatus, as in Fig. 5.3, like a large gas fire in appearance, with a radiant section but chiefly capable of making enough warm air for the entire house. Open doors are the principal means of air movement, and many people say that the results are much more uniform than might be expected.

How do gas and electric room heaters compare?

Electric heaters use the heat storage principle, gas is instant.

Electric heaters need no flue, and may stand anywhere. Gas heaters have a balanced flue and need an outside wall.

Both have models with varying degrees of controllability built in. Thus, electric heaters, which are electric storage radiators, are in their basic form without any form of heat outlet control other than the insulation which determines the natural rate of heat loss. But in a better form they have a

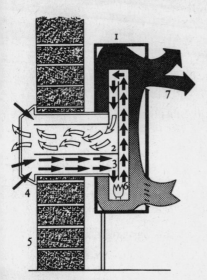

1. The heater installed within the room
2. Outlet duct (products of combustion)
3. Inlet duct (air for combustion)
4. External wall grille
5. Suitable outside wall
6. Combustion chamber and heat exchanger
7. Natural convection movement

Fig. 5.4 Balanced flue operation and air flow in gas convector (Drugasar Ltd)

means of controlling the air flow through the heated core:
either by a damper which is usually manually operated, or by a
fan which is started and stopped by room thermostat and clock.
Similarly, the gas convector heater in its basic form has simply
a gas cock, which controls the amount of gas to the main
burner, or, much better, it may have a non-electric thermostat

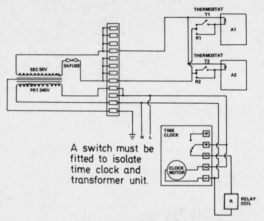

*Figure 5.5   Controlling 2 gas convectors with one clock
and 2 wall mounted room thermostats (Drugasar Ltd)*

incorporated. However, by involving electricity, the heater
may be controlled by clock and room thermostat, though this
degree of control is so far exercised external to the unit
(Fig. 5.5). It is particularly suited to controlling more than
one unit, if only because it spreads the cost of the extra
equipment. (It will be seen that the increasing cost of all fuels
will erode the advantage which appears to exist in buying the
elementary version of either of the above units.)

How much space do the various heating units require?

The gas fired heater for a full system is usually of vertical
column form, as shown in Fig. 5.6. With a return air duct, it

will occupy most of a room height, and measure in the region of 600 mm (24 in) from back to front, and perhaps 500 mm (20 in) across. An Electricaire unit, the electrical equivalent, may be of the same shape and size, or it may look more like a chest freezer, being horizontal. These dimensions will apply to stub duct units too.

The oil fired hearth unit may be said to take up no space at all, since the space occupied could not be used for other purposes.

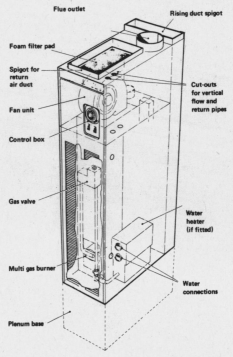

Figure 5.6   Gas-fired warm air heater – downflow, with cover off

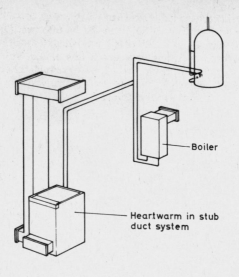

Boiler

Heartwarm in stub duct system

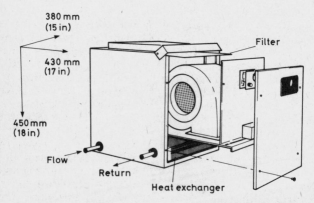

380 mm (15 in)

430 mm (17 in)

450 mm (18 in)

Filter

Flow

Return

Heat exchanger

Figure 5.7   The heartwarm air and water heater system in a stub duct system (Massrealm Ltd)

Electric storage radiators tend to be bulky as well as heavy, and a model with 3 kW input might be 600 mm (24 in) tall, the same across, and half that from back to front. A typical gas convector, weighing very much less and in any case not depending upon a floor for support, would measure from 400 mm (15 in) high, by 300 mm (12 in) wide, by 125 mm (5 in) deep, for the smaller models.

How do units compare economically?

Electrical units run off cheaper current, the basis of charging being the 'off-peak' principle. Although the details tend to vary, the principle is to encourage, by pricing, the use of electricity during the night hours, when expensive plant is otherwise idling and waiting for the peak loads for which it is installed. The price advantage was once almost lost by political action, and intending users should make careful enquiries about both tariffs and their durability. Electrical power at standard rates would be prohibitively expensive.

It should be borne in mind, to electricity's advantage, that in use it must be reckoned 100% efficient, since all the heat put in comes out again into the room.

Gas pricing has no surprises, being charged at the ruling rate for all domestic prices. The efficiency of most wall convectors is about 75%, in line with the best of gas appliances. The oil convector shown here is likely to have a lower but variable efficiency, perhaps 65–70% depending upon whether it is adjusted for maximum radiation or maximum convection. The addition of a back boiler will add to the overall efficiency, but the intending buyer of a back boiler should seek assurances about oil supplies. If fuel is not available, efficiency is irrelevant.

Aside from the fundamental economics, we must take account of the economics of real operation, which are dependent upon the degree of controllability. This favours full duct system units, both gas and electric, fan controlled electric storage radiators, and where applicable gas convectors, with added controls or (when available) those with integral controls.

6

THE FUELS

What fuels?

There are the so-called fossil fuels. These are: coal, coke, and prepared solid fuels such as Coalite and briquettes; natural gas and bottled gas; oil, in the form of paraffin, domestic heating oil (class C) or gas oil (class D). We also include electricity, still mainly made from fossil fuels though it is a refined form of energy.

What about solar energy?

It is unlikely that solar energy will be available in the quantity required for house heating, in winter in UK. Even in summer it mainly augments, not entirely displaces, the other means of making domestic hot water.

Which fuel should I choose?

This once straightforward subject is now complicated by threats of permanent scarcity. The first job, from now on, when choosing a fuel must be to make enquiries about getting a supply into the foreseeable future. Ask then, if you dare, about its future price.

Gas, it is said, will last for another 30 years. Bottled gas comes from oil, so is not necessarily an automatic substitute for places where there is no gas main.

Coal does not give rise to such anxieties, being assured for 300 years. Nevertheless, if you contemplate using some such fuel as anthracite or one of the prepared fuels, make sure first that it is obtainable locally, particularly in smaller communities.

If available, which fuel is best?

They all have their virtues. Two, oil and solid, you store and can therefore live through a period of crisis, strike or other breakdown in services. But most modern oil appliances, along with gas boilers, depend upon electricity for running. Fortunately, electricity supply is nowadays very reliable.

For the utmost reliability, then, it would seem that solid fuel is top. On other counts it is less attractive, being both heavy and dirty to handle, and requiring disposal of the ash. It is also, by comparison, a coarse fuel, not amenable to instant automatic control as the others are. Nevertheless, it is the longest lived, and has never lost its popularity. It is now served by a new generation of appliances, some of them designed specifically to enable the smoke producing coals to be burned without trouble in smokeless zones.

Oil and gas have features in common, notably that both may be finely controlled by instrumentation, allowing the use of the most up-to-date heat emission equipment. Gas offers a somewhat larger choice of appliances, including those with balanced flue (which oil has to a limited extent only).

Electricity may be said to take two forms, in the important matter of cost. Current at the standard tariff is scarcely to be contemplated nowadays, except as a standby, for instance an electric fire used for a short period around bedtime. At the reduced offpeak rate it becomes practical, and is used in storage radiators and Electricaire units.

This is but the scantiest review, and shows that there is no one best fuel.

How would personal factors affect choice of fuel?

Possibly quite a lot. Are you, for instance, getting towards retirement age, or physically handicapped, or even just unwilling to exert yourself? Then you will not choose to lift solid fuel and ash, and clean out grates and firebeds.

Do you own the house you live in, or only rent it? In the second case, you will not wish to put in capital equipment unless you have an agreement with the landlord to offset it against rent, or some other such arrangement. You will, then, put in some system which is mainly removable if you leave. This could be electric storage radiators, or gas fires. It could be one or more free standing solid fuel stoves, without back boiler. It could be an oil fired hearth unit, like a large gas fire, generating enough warm air to circulate all over the house.

Another factor is the type of property. In a flat you cannot store oil, probably not solid fuel. But in both cases, would there be a chimney to use? (Gas can have a balanced flue, and electricity no flue at all.) Some new houses are being built without a chimney. Fortunately one can be added using modern systems.

7

DOMESTIC HOT WATER

What does domestic hot water have to do with central heating?

The connection is not logical but it is very convenient. In the most popular form of heating, the wet system, the boiler takes care of both functions. It is also entirely relevant that hot water (dhw) takes precedence. Nobody, we think, has central heating but no hot water at home.

In systems which do not include a boiler it is usual for dhw to be made by the same form of energy which heats the system. This is to get any discount for quantity buying of fuel. In some cases, as in remote cottages, there might be no choice of fuels.

But none of these considerations prevent us from looking at cases where dhw may have to be produced on its own.

How much domestic hot water does an average household need?

The average household has two parents and 2.3 children, but any number of children from nil to three would be reasonably served by a cylinder of hot water capacity about 30 gal with a recovery rate of about 3 kW or 10 000 Btu/h. There is no denying that, at times, this will create frustrations. But there will be many more times when the system will be at standby, waiting for use. It is a matter of economic good sense. There exists a 'scientific' means of estimating requirements, which allocates fixed quantities to man, woman and child, with allowances for the washing machine, the dish washer, and so on. However, the usefulness of this method is open to grave doubt.

It must be remembered that some families bath daily, others do not. Some take showers instead or as well, and you can have five or six showers for one bath. You might say that a family with four children needs a larger cylinder and greater make-up rate. But suppose they all take showers?

Can the system's capacity be stretched, e.g. in an emergency?

Because a shower uses one sixth of the water that a bath uses showers are important, for fuel and for water when short. In a similar way there are taps which are built for economy, which allow hand washing under a well designed spray instead of running a conventional tap full bore. Remember too, if faced with a fuel shortage or a house full of relations, that the dish washer is a glutton for hot water. Try old fashioned washing up for a few days. The automatic washing machine is also wasteful, though cold rinses are more wasteful of water than of heat.

When it comes to operating the system, a substantial increase in capacity can be achieved simply by turning up the thermostat. For example, if water is stored at 80°C (180°F) instead of at 60°C (140°F) the thermal capacity of the system is increased by about 40%.

Warning: Do not allow children, invalids or others of diminished responsibility to have access to very hot water.

How does a wet heating system make hot water?

Fig. 7.1 shows a small bore heating system, with on the left of the boiler a separate gravity circuit feeding the heat exchanger inside an indirect hot water cylinder (Figs. 7.2, 7.3 and 7.4). The circuit is not subject to the long and often tortuous runs which a heating system has to undertake. The short direct route is indeed a condition of installation. Consequently the disadvantages which have caused the gravity wet system to be abandoned do not apply with any great force.

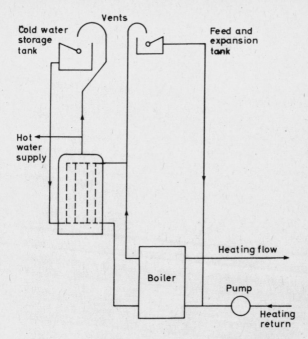

Figure 7.1   Main features of a typical combined small-bore heating and hot water supply system

Nevertheless progress has been made, and the pumped primary system exists. It is associated, for instance, with automatic boilers of very low water capacity in which rapid water velocity is essential. The extra measure of control which it confers is used to give a choice. By means of a priority switch the user may choose to divert the major effort at any one time to either heating or hot water. This makes for rapid recovery times when needed.

Note: gravity primaries are *not* small bore! They are usually 1 inch (28 mm copper).

91

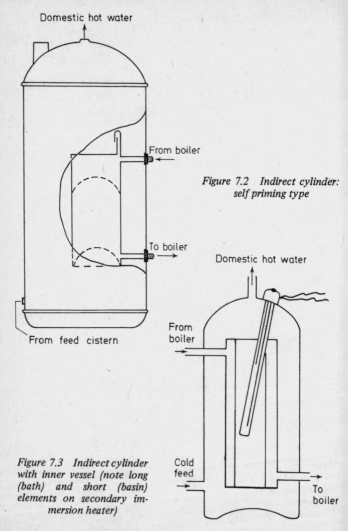

Domestic hot water

From boiler →

Figure 7.2   Indirect cylinder: self priming type

To boiler →

From feed cistern

Domestic hot water

From boiler →

Figure 7.3   Indirect cylinder with inner vessel (note long (bath) and short (basin) elements on secondary immersion heater)

Cold feed →

To boiler →

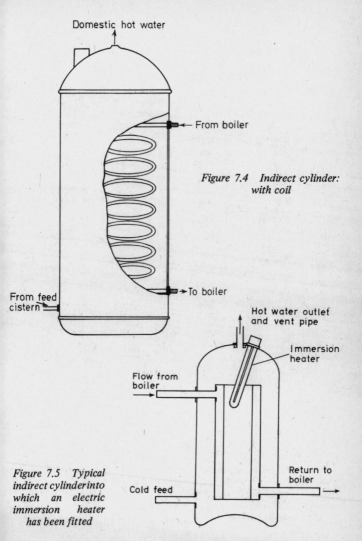

Domestic hot water

From boiler

Figure 7.4 Indirect cylinder: with coil

From feed cistern

To boiler

Hot water outlet and vent pipe

Immersion heater

Flow from boiler

Return to boiler

Figure 7.5 Typical indirect cylinder into which an electric immersion heater has been fitted

Cold feed

What happens when the heating system is dry or 'heating only'?

Then hot water may be any system, and the choice is often guided by the fuel which has been chosen for the heating system.

The choice may fall on a solid fuel back boiler, particularly if one is already installed. It would rarely be chosen otherwise, for the limited duty, because it might very well produce more hot water than needed at off peak times.

One popular standby is the electric immersion heater (Fig. 7.5). It costs very little to buy and install, even though its running cost is high. Running cost may be reduced if the heating system is electric, by arrangement, whereby the immersion

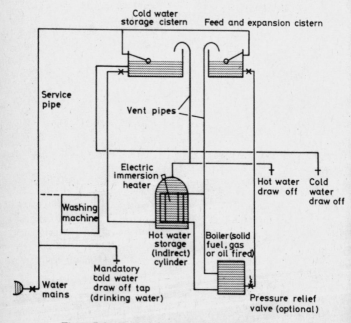

Figure 7.6   Typical domestic water installation

heater is used on the cheaper tariff. A larger hot water cylinder may be required, to store hot water for peak hours.

One way to improve the useful efficiency of an immersion heater is to have a duplex one, with two heaters, one long and one short. This requires a boss in the top of the cylinder, the two heaters reaching downwards. The shorter one is switched on for small quantities, labelled Basin, and the longer one for Baths (Fig. 7.3).

Gas offers two systems. The one is a miniature boiler, usually called a circulator, whose rated output is likely to be in the range 3—5 kW, or 10 000—16 000 Btu/h. This is thermostatically controlled, and will work hard to restore the temperature in a run down cylinder, then shut itself off.

The other device is the now well known instantaneous gas water heater, multipoint version. This lights when the opening of a tap anywhere in the hot water system causes a drop in water pressure at the heater. The gas valve opens, the pilot ignites the main burner, and hot water is produced instantaneously until the closing of the tap causes a rise in pressure which shuts the gas valve again.

Any of these methods may be used in circumstances where there is no heating system.

Is instantaneous heating more efficient than having a storage cylinder?

The answer is bound to be yes. However well a cylinder is lagged it does lose heat. However, if this stray heat is usefully employed, as it usually is in keeping an airing cupboard warm, then the loss of efficiency is bearable. In this connection, it must be said that inadequate lagging should not be used, to encourage heat leak in an airing cupboard. Lag your best and enough heat will still get out.

Although it may seem that we ought to abandon cylinders in favour of instantaneous heaters, let us not forget convenience of use. The best of instantaneous heaters are a bit slow at bath filling, and sometimes we are in a hurry.

Is it more efficient to leave an immersion heater on all the time, or to switch it on when required?

This favourite question threatens to confuse efficiency with convenience. An immersion heater has its own thermostat, and once switched on may be left and forgotten, and, withdrawals excepted, hot water will always be available. Thus, for most of the time, the stored water will be at its hottest. Nothing could be more convenient.

There is, however, a law of physics which states that the rate of cooling is proportional to the excess temperature, i.e. the amount by which the hot temperature exceeds the cold temperature, which in this case is the air outside the cylinder. So, a cylinder which is most of the time at maximum temperature has most of the time the greatest excess, and so the greatest heat loss. By contrast, an immersion heater which is switched on as needed is rarely at maximum temperature, because the hot water is wanted as made, and is drawn off. The inconvenience of being efficient can be largely offset, however, if the job of switching on is given to a clock. Most of us want hot water first thing in the morning, and at some time in the evening, a fairly regular programme.

Is there a best temperature for domestic hot water?

The main considerations are: Safety i.e. avoidance of exposing anyone to contact with scalding hot water; Heat conservation; the cooling law mentioned in the last answer shows how heat is saved by lowering the temperature gap; Scaling, a hard water will deposit less scale at lower temperatures. All these factors point to a moderately low temperature, which we would set in the region of 60°C (140°F).

It happens that certain dish washing machines specify a higher water temperature, and this will need to be borne in mind. Also, as mentioned elsewhere, some flexibility, a willingness to set the temperature high at times, increases the heat capacity of the storage.

How can dhw be stored at 60°C (140°F) if the wet central heating is at 80°C (180°F)?

By fitting a cylinder thermostat. This, which may be a strap-on unit, operates a solenoid valve in the primary. When the chosen temperature is reached, the dhw primary circulation is stopped until the temperature falls again.

Is there a best system for producing hot water?

As with central heating, a lot depends upon local circumstances, personal preferences etc, but this is another area where we are torn between efficiency and convenience. The author's preference is for the well insulated cylinder served by an independent gas circulator. It is certain that dhw is best served by its own apparatus. It has nothing in common with the heating load, being often an embarrassing extra burden in winter, and a means of keeping the boiler at work on about 20% capacity in summer. This is a direct cause of inefficiency, and hot water becomes expensive.

Why do not more people adopt separate systems?

There are inconveniences and disadvantages: first cost, the need for two flues, more space taken in inadequate premises. However, the advantages outweigh these inconveniences and more people would adopt separate systems if they knew about them.

What part can electricity play in domestic water heating?

The obvious apparatus is the immersion heater, which has been mentioned. Although one associates immersion heaters with the hot water cylinder, the principle is in fact greatly extended in practice. We have only to think of the popular under-sink heater, or the under-basin heater, the udb where db stands for draining board. They are an immersion heater in a suitably styled and sized insulated container. It is very important to

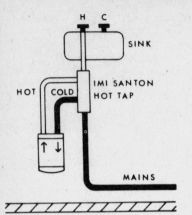

Figure 7.7 Under-sink heater with special IMI Santon hot tap — no vent pipe required

TYPICAL PIPE LAYOUT FOR
NON-PRESSURE TYPE APPLICATION

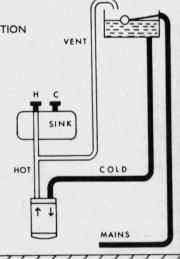

Figure 7.8 Under-sink heater with standard sink (or basin) taps, with vent pipe

TYPICAL PIPE LAYOUT FOR
PRESSURE TYPE APPLICATION

note that all of these, unless otherwise stated, are low pressure vessels. That means that they are designed for pressures developed by a cistern fed system of two or three storeys height. They are *not* designed to withstand mains pressure. If in any doubt, consult the electricity board in your area (Figs. 7.7, 7.8 and 7.9).

Figure 7.9   The Unatap, from Walker Crosweller Co Ltd, is particularly suited to a udb heater, which cuts out time and fuel-wasting 'dead leg'. It gives maximum economy in use

A special case is the instantaneous electric shower. This is almost useless for any other application, except one in which the same spray can be used — shampoo, hand rinsing, jobs of that kind. It depends for its usefulness upon the water being discharged through a shower rose specially designed to make the most of very little water.

Why do electrically heated showers give very little water?

The obvious first step, to attract business and indeed to please the electricity supply authority, is to make the system fit into the limits of an ordinary domestic electricity supply. This, you will recall, envisages the greatest domestic load to come from the electric cooker, for which a 30 A fuse is provided. The greatest load which can be applied to a single phase domestic supply fused 30 A is about 7 kW. That, then, is the maximum power input available. It is easy to convert this into water raised from cold to shower temperature, and the amount is around 1.6 litre (6 pints) per minute. This is not inconsiderable, but not much practical use unless properly presented, which is why electric showers have their own design of shower rose. It is not suitable to connect such a heater to a conventional shower set.

How much water does a conventional shower use?

Most makers of shower equipment make a shower head or rose which will deliver, quite adequately and acceptably, about 2.7 litres (1¼ gal) per minute. There are models with greater natural output, even in this country, while in America the average rate of output seems as likely to drown as to wash the subject. However, as long as a rate around 2.5 litres per minute is satisfactory it would be folly to use more.

At higher supply pressures all such equipment will give a greater output, unless checked. In that case, why not check it?

How much of the output is hot water?

There is a simple equation governing heat exchanges:

Heat lost by hot water = heat gained by cold water
(when hot and cold water are mixed, as in a shower valve).
Mass of hw × fall in temp. = mass of cw × rise in temp.

If we take the hw temperature as 60°C: cold as 10°C; shower (mixed) as 40°C;

Then
$$\frac{\text{mass of hw}}{\text{mass of cw}} = \frac{40 - 10}{60 - 40} = \frac{3}{2}$$

In the example chosen, therefore, 60% of the total is hot water.

Are the claims made for showers justified?

The case has not been overstated. Showers are hygienic and economical, saving usually some 80% of the water a bath would use. Installation costs less than a bath does. The cost of adding showering facilities to an existing bath can pay for itself in running cost in a relatively short time.

8

CONTROLS

Is it true that the more controls the more efficient the system?

No. Controls can be set to produce extravagance as well as economy. Sometimes controls can quarrel over the same function, and then neither does the job.

What are the essential controls?

Consider first what they have to do. Comfort with economy consists in having (a) as much warmth as you need but no more, (b) warmth when you need it, and at no other time, and (c) warmth where you need it, nowhere else.

The basic equipment for (a) is a thermostat. It will be a room thermostat, usually controlling a circulating pump, or a radiator valve, or a warm air shutter, or the fan of a fan convector.

The time control is an obvious case for clock control. In the case of boilers it is often incorporated within a programmer. It cannot do anything for a solid fuel boiler unless that happens to be a complex unit, with screw feed, or fan propelled air — an electric motor which can be switched off.

(c) is not so easily managed. Man is mobile, and should train himself to treat heating like lighting, and turn it on and off in each room. But the case for 'where' is often averaged, and then mixed with (b). For example, if you nearly always retire to the lounge at seven, at six thirty the fan convector in the lounge should be switched on by a clock.

Can we usefully separate 'day' rooms from 'night' rooms?

Very usefully, and usually fairly simply, because most houses segregate the two into downstairs and upstairs. This calls for zone control, and zone controllers such as the Satchwell Minival. This device switches circuits on a time basis which the

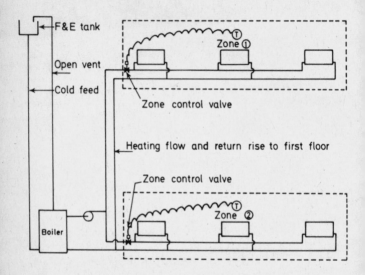

Figure 8.1   A form of zone control

user decides. It can often be added with minimum alteration to the pipe circuit. It produces, in effect, a mechanised form of selective heating.

Fig. 8.1 shows a form of zone control which has, instead of a single change-over controller, two controllers acting independently in the upper and lower zones. Such a system would cope very well with overlapping zone operation times, and the controller T is a clock.

Can we choose the controls to have on the heater?

The heater is the boiler, or warm air unit, or other heat source, and these units are designed and built with the necessary controls incorporated. No changes may be made to these, since safety is one of the factors involved. But appliances which use the refined fuels, i.e. not solid fuel, usually have electrical control systems. When this occurs it is quite common for an electrical junction box to be physically incorporated in the casing, while not being an integral part of the heater.

What is the function of such an electrical junction box?

It serves as the current input point, and the output to the heater. But, in addition, it may be electrically designed so that many other controls, of which the clock is a ready example, may be wired in series with the output and act as a secondary

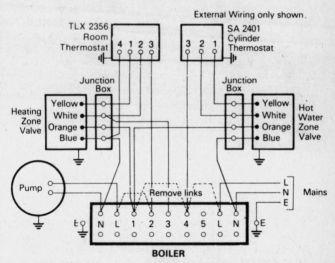

Figure 8.2 Typical wiring diagram of electric centre, for pumped primary system, with various controls (Thorn Heating Ltd)

switch. Many quite ingenious combinations have been worked out in this way by some manufacturers. They are presented to the customer as 'what the heater will do' (Fig. 8.2).

Can a solid fuel heated system have controls?

The example nearest to mind is the small bore system heated by a solid fuel boiler or back boiler. Its pump can be controlled on/off by a room thermostat *provided that* the system includes a gravity hot water system with cylinder. The pump can also have clock control. It is possible, given the same essential condition, to use thermostatic radiator valves on such a system. These are generally non-electric.

Does a system with radiator thermostats need a roomstat as well?

It does not need one, and such a system is expected to have a continuously running pump controlled only by a clock. A roomstat would be extra expense, as well as offering a possibility of 'hunting', which is an unwelcome condition where two controllers try to do the same job and trip each other up. In spite of this, some installers use a roomstat, presumably as a last ditch control, and they set it to a temperature higher than the radstats so that it does not normally cut out, if ever.

How can the clock controller be used to assist in economical running?

The first thing it does is to remember, particularly, to shut off. Elsewhere we have suggested certain timings. In answering a question about programmer settings, we suggested that a family getting up at 7.30 should set the boiler to on at 6.30. The first thing a prudent householder should do is to try to prove us wrong. He should set his boiler to come on at 7.00 instead, and then see whether the house and the hot water are satisfactory. If they are, he has saved a half hour running. And so on. Try shutting down half an hour *before* bed time. It is in every case a matter of experimenting, and well worth it.

What can be saved by thoughtful use of the room thermostat?

Ask yourself, do you tend to wallow in warmth? Do you still believe that you should be able to wear swimming trunks indoors, instead of keeping a pullover on? If so, just try remembering that every 1 deg C of heating in the area we are considering is worth 7% of the total fuel bill. Either you turn it up, and it costs you that, or you turn it down and you save 7%. The trouble about central heating is that it is addictive. We might catch cold less easily if there were less difference between indoor and outdoor temperatures. So turn it down a little and see whether anyone notices.

What can a cylinder thermostat save?

The best temperature for storing hot water is usually in the $60°C$ ($140°F$) range. This is somewhat lower than is needed to fulfil the design conditions of the heating system. But the cylinderstat will permit both temperatures to operate together, and the economical thing about $60°C$ is that the standing loss from the hot water in store is considerably less than it would be at say $80°C$.

Can the boiler thermostat save anything?

Given a full set of controls as outlined above, it cannot. It should be set high, so that all the other controls may have something to work on.

Can a ducted warm air heater be used economically?

It is subject to control by both clock and roomstat, and earlier remarks about both these apply equally to air heaters. A fully ducted air system has an extra quality, derived from the fact that it is handling direct the warming medium, air. At certain times and in quite a lot of places, one or more rooms being warmed will be subjected to sunshine, causing solar gain. Such rooms will have warmer air than average. But this will be returned and redistributed, to the general benefit. It will generally cause an earlier response from the roomstat wherever that may be situated. The same applies to any incidental access of warmth from whatever source.

What developments may be expected in controls, to aid economy?

If the present range of controls, apparently quite extensive in function, has a drawback it may be said to be inflexibility. A control obeys the last order, irrespective of any change in circumstances which may have occurred. The flexibility has at present still to be supplied by the human being in charge. The only way a machine can exhibit flexibility, by taking into account a number of variables, is for it to be a computer. It will not be many years, in our view, before some boilers are equipped with a form of mini-computer, based on modern electronic components, to control operation in the light of room conditions at any given time.

9

SOME USEFUL CALCULATIONS

How do we calculate heat losses?

The method should become quite clear if you follow the
directions given and fill in the Heat Loss Sheet (Fig. 9.1). It
will be seen that each room is treated separately and its total
heat loss, i.e. required heat input, is found. When all rooms
have been calculated, the totals are to be added, to give the
grand total which is the required heat input for the whole
house.

*Does this sheet apply to warm air heating as well as to wet
systems?*

It applies to any form of heating. Heat loss is quite independent
of types of heating system.

Is the sheet for a full central heating system?

That is entirely up to you. If it is for a full system, you will
make out a heat loss table for every room, hall etc. You will
do the same if it is for background or selective heating. But if
it is for partial heating only, then you will calculate for only
those rooms which you decide to warm.

*How can it apply to full as well as to background and selective
heating?*

Looking at the instructions you will find that certain factors
have to be put in. The physical measurements of rooms are

fixed. But, for example in Note 2, you must fill in the design temperature. This will be in all cases lower for background heating.

The reason for doing a full survey for selective heating is that every room will need a heat emitter (radiator or the like). It is only the full total which will show selection. The full total is arrived at by adding together only those rooms which will form the nucleus of the heating system by being on together at any one time.

HEAT LOSS SHEET
Design outdoor temperature −1°C

		Lounge			*Dining*		
1.	Room						
2.	Design room temperature						
3.	Design temp. diff. degC						
4.	Room length . .m						
5.	Room width . . .m						
6.	Outside walls, long. .m						
7.	Room height . . .m						
		Area	U value	kW	Area	U value	kW
8.	Outside walls, total						
9.	Windows						
10.	Outside doors						
11.	9 + 10						
12.	8 − 11						
13.	Unwarmed wall						
14.	Unwarmed floor						
15.	Unwarmed ceiling						
16.	Reqd. air changes						
17.	Room vol. 4 x 5 x 7						
18.	Air heat loss						
19.	Total heat loss						
20.	Allowance						
21.	Design heat loss						

If using Imperial units then: Design outdoor temperature is 30°F: physical measurements are in feet, and areas in ft². U values are Imperial: heat loss is Btu/h.

Fig. 9.1. The heat loss design sheet and how to complete it

To use the Heat Loss sheet: calculate each room independently, then complete lines as follows:

1. Identify room, as kitchen, Bedroom 1 etc.
2. Design temperature for that room. See Chapter 1.
3. Difference between 2. and outside design temperature.
4.5. Longest wall and other wall.
6. Total of outside walls.
7. Height of room.
8. 6 x 7.
9. Area of windows, and U-value. kW column*: area x U-value x line 3.
10. Outside doors, as for windows line 9.
11. Add areas of 9 and 10.
12. Subtract line 11 from line 8 (area). Add U-value of walls. kW column*: area x U-value x line 3.
13. If next door is a room or space at lower temperature heat will pass. Enter Partition area, and U-value, kW column*: area x U-value x line 3. If next door is unheated, assume halfway to cold.
14. 4 x 5 x floor U-value. kW column*: area x U-value x line 3.
15. as 14 but for ceiling.
16. Air changes, average 1.5 per hour.
17. 4 x 5 x 7.
18. Line 17 x line 16 x line 3 x 0.33 (for Btu/h use 0.02, not 0.33.)
19. Add all the kW column figures.
20. An allowance may be up to 10% of line 19. We have indicated elsewhere our dislike of allowances, except in ·the case of selective heating, or where rapid warm-up is wanted and means exist to cut back to a 'normal' rate (as with thermostatic radiator valves).
21. Sum of lines 19 and 20 if applicable.

* The result of the calculation is in watts. Divide by 1000 before entering in the kW column in the table opposite.

How does the sheet differentiate between houses which have been well insulated, and others?

This is another case of inserting factors which you supply. These are the *U* values, which go in the central column. Some common *U* values are given in Table 9.1. The figure represents the heat loss through a given substance, e.g. house wall or window, and the lower the figure the better. For more information on *U* values consult the *Guide to Good Practice* published by the Chartered Institution of Building Services. A public library should be able to obtain a copy. But if you have had any special treatment, for example a proprietary cavity wall filling, you should ask the contractor to tell you what he expects the U value of the walls now is. It is very important to take account of all such benefits, in order to construct a realistic heat balance and buy an appropriately smaller heat generator.

Table 9.1 SOME U VALUES

(In spite of the now speedy transfer of calculations to metric units we respect the preference of those who still think in Imperial. This table shows both sets of units)
   Note: only external walls have the low temperature on the outside. Internal or partition walls have some indoor temperature, and the heat loss is less though the U value is not altered by this fact. Total heat loss is a product of U x area x temp. difference.

Type of construction	U value	
	Metric	*Imperial*
External wall, plastered brick		
4½ in	3.2	0.57
9 in	2.4	0.43
11 in cavity unventilated	1.7	0.30
do ventilated	1.95	0.34
Window single glazed	5.7	1.0
double	2.9	0.5
Partition wall plastered brick		
4½ in	2.55	0.45
9 in	2.1	0.37
Pitched roof		
Tile on board & felt	2.0	0.35
Plasterboard ceiling, roof space		
over: 2 in vermiculite infill	0.8	0.14
Ground floor		
Suspended, single air brick	1.7	0.30
ditto with parquet, lino etc.	1.4	0.25
Solid floor on earth	1.15	0.20

Should we take the outside design temperature as $-1°C$ or $30°F$

In so far as these tables are official policy, there has been no change yet. But this is an area in which the common sense and commercial prudence of the householder might well take over. We do have occasional cold winters, but for the majority of most winters the outdoor temperature is down to freezing for a minority of the time. Thus, an underestimated heat loss caused by taking the outdoor design temperature as, say, $4-5°C$, might cause mild discomfort indoors for some of the time. The householder at least could warm himself with the thought of the saving of fuel.

What is the simplest way to make savings?

Using an outdoor design temperature of $4-5°C$ is one way of saving fuel, but it is not the simplest. The simplest way to arrive at the full total, on which boiler or heater size is based, and then *do not add* any margin. Instead, subtract something. What you could subtract is the heat requirement of rooms which need not be heated at the same time as all other rooms – the spare bedroom, or indeed any bedrooms in daytime, the hobbies room perhaps. In short, opt for a selective system after all. If you are like most people, you simply do not occupy all the rooms in the house at the same time. So why not use your heating as you use your lighting, and turn it on when you want it?

Suppose I want to use all the rooms?

Turning up the boiler thermostat will make what you have got go further, in the case of a wet system. But it must be said that anyone just starting out to have a family had better take all this advice about cutting back with caution. If the use of more rooms is in prospect, it would be difficult to extend the heating system later.

How accurate are the heat loss figures obtained by using the sheet?

They are moderately accurate, although some quite normal event such as opening a window in face of a freezing wind can make nonsense of them, for an hour or more.

We would not recommend, though, that each room total be adjusted to a round figure. It could very well result in every room being rounded up (or down) with the result that the grand total would be very considerably high (or low). The best method is to proceed as though each room were as calculated, and do any rounding off only to the grand total.

How much rounding off is advisable?

The easiest first step is to do away with fractions of a kW other than 0.5, and all Btu/h below 100 if using imperial units. Other simplifications will follow inevitably, as will be shown. It is a good rule, when rounding off on the limited lines indicated, to round up. For example, 2.43 kW will become 2.5 kW and 7.223 Btu/h will become 7.300 Btu/h. We know then that we have something in hand if the apparatus on offer is a little below our target.

How is the table used to choose a radiator?

Quite simply by reading off a manufacturer's list. Any radiator manufacturer who is a member of MARC will give a list of radiator sizes with outputs under standard conditions of use. The object of the exercise is to find a radiator which is of roughly the right heat output, and also the right size for the space you have in mind to put it. For more output from less wall space, there are double panels. Larger than calculated radiators may be used if they are to be controlled by thermostatic radiator valves.

What are 'standard' conditions of use?

In this connection the one that matters is the difference between inside the radiator (hot water) and outside (the air). Figures are based upon this being 55 deg C (100 deg F). Factors may be applied for higher or lower differentials.

Are skirting heaters classified in the same way?

It is more usual to find that each make or brand has a heat emission 'per metre (or ft) run'. A typical figure is 450, in both scales. The object is then to buy the length needed, if there is enough wall to fit it on.

Do natural convectors resemble radiators?

They do not. The choice is very limited, whereas radiator choice is wide. Convectors rely therefore upon individual control, often manual, to match their performance to requirements at any one time. Consequently oversizing is no great disadvantage.

What about fan convectors?

Oversizing, again within the limited range of choice, is helpful with rapid room warming using fan convectors. These appliances include thermostatic control, and most also have fan speed control. This should be used to modify the fan speed/heat output so that the thermostat cuts off heating for short periods only. If it does not cut off at all the heat output is too low, through too slow fan speed or too cool water, probably. But if it cuts off for, say, 30 minutes in every hour the room temperature will experience peaks and troughs, despite the thermostat.

Does a 3 kW electric storage radiator give out 3 kW?

This is the odd man out, where everything is measured as input. Thus, it is the charge rate which is 3 kW. If the charging period is 8 hours the total charge can amount to 3 × 8 = 24 kWh. If this were given off evenly over 24 hours, which of course if it not, the output would be 1 kW. Better consult the local Electricity Board when choosing one of these.

How does one choose a gas fired unit heater?

This too is a matter best discussed with the local gas people, not least because choice is still very limited. As noted previously, these devices are still simple, lacking much instrumentation and control is likely to be manual.

What determines the size of warm air registers?

A rough answer to this question is that the *free area* of the register must be of a size to pass the calculated amount of warm air, at a velocity which must lie within the limits of 1.0 − 2.0 m/s. But for all matters connected with ducted warm air we recommend reading the Design Manual issued by the Society of British Gas Industries (Benn).

10

SOME CONCLUSIONS

Where can I go for impartial advice?

Almost nowhere. Anyone with the slightest interest in or knowledge of the subject is bound to have preferences or prejudices. The condition to be avoided is commercial involvement, and the technical advice service of one of the better class magazines is as good as anywhere.

Is not impartial advice necessary, to avoid being manipulated?

No. To avoid being manipulated unknowingly you need knowledge. Armed with that you need not fear the half truths and glowing hyperboles of salesmen. You can indeed benefit from them because you are able to ask critical questions, to weigh statements and compare claims. It is also a self-generating success, because a salesman will not persist in too much 'selling' if he realises that you are on equal terms with him. Enough knowledge is not hard to come by. Some you will get from reading this book. For a fuller account you should read *Beginner's Guide to Central Heating* and *Beginner's Guide to Home Energy Saving* (Newnes Technical Books).

How do I start to choose a heating system for my house?

The best way is to eliminate the non-starters. For example, flat dwellers cannot have an oil storage tank, villagers with no gas cannot have gas, houses with no electricity can have practically nothing, except a solid fuel appliance and a wet gravity system. Remember, too, to take due account of the prejudices which constitute non-starters. Some people would not have gas at any price, or solid fuel because it means carrying, storing, and so on. That accounts for fuels. As for systems, most people can say with some assurance that a ducted warm air system would be too obstructive in an existing house, though a stub duct system might suit.

How should I tackle the short list?

There is no 'best' system except in so far as you decide. So you must weigh up the pros and cons of wet and dry systems, decide whether you want domestic hot water built in (which means a wet system) or independent (which might be either). If you decide upon a wet system, will it be small bore single or two-pipe or microbore? Which fuel will you have, and what class of boiler? Or, as a dry system, do you want air delivered in ducts, either full or stub; or would you prefer it made room by room, by electric storage radiators or gas fired unit (wall) heaters?

And will you then consider quantities, and decide whether to have a full system, or partial or background or selective, or some mongrel from these?

Once you have at least partly answered these questions, you should have reached a very short list. It is now up to you to shop around and see where you can get the best terms, and the best promise of continuing good terms. For at that stage the technicalities of the subject have ceased to matter.

With cost a consideration, is it wise to do the work myself?

Perhaps not wise, but in a number of cases it is possible, as has been shown. But people with no mechanical aptitude should not attempt complicated work. There is after all a lot of money to lose, and the cost of rectifying mistakes could be large. For the capable person, the handyman press often carries advertisements by firms who will do designs, and supply all the materials, with instructions. There are other firms who sell proprietary goods at quite high discounts, while designs may be had from firms selling these. All these schemes reduce the labour cost of the job.

Where should I go to get the job done for me?

For any type of system you may employ a contractor who is a member of HVCA (Heating and Ventilating Contractors' Association). They will direct you to an appropriate specialist if necessary, and they operate a very useful Guarantee scheme which safeguards you.

For gas fired systems only, it is best to choose someone who is registered with CORGI, as the gas industry themselves are. Everyone registered has to maintain a consistent standard of work and the customer can appeal if he is not satisfied. CORGI is the Confederation of Registered Gas Installers, and the nearest gas showroom has details.

In our experience far too little use is made of the advisory services to be had from fuel suppliers, particularly gas and electricity.

It is important to remember that there is advice to be had for the asking, and there are installers who demonstrate their faith in themselves by belonging to reputable associations. And any installer who is competent can join. There is no sense therefore in having such expensive work done by just anybody who happens to apply for it.

The insulation of cavity walls, not possible for the amateur, should be entrusted to a member firm of NCIA (National Cavity Insulation Association).

What about servicing?

Automatic equipment, e.g. gas and oil fired boilers, must have regular service. This can be arranged with the installer, or in the case of gas with the gas people. Usually you have the choice of initiating it yourself as necessary, or putting it on contract in which case they will remember for you. The contract is worth while so long as it is not too one-sided. It should include for a certain amount of material, unless very low priced, or it should include a guarantee against breakdown of serviced items between servicings.

If you usually service your own car you should be able to do most of the work yourself, but you should lay in a stock of essential spares. The service department of the manufacturer will be able to advise you what you should have, and it is useful to know what to ask the local people for.

Could I not deal direct with the manufacturers?

It is not usual. Information you can get, and sometimes the state of local knowledge is such that you need to do this, but there is usually an agreement in existence whereby merchants and nationalised industries are the customers of the manufacturers, and the public buys from these. If manufacturers had to enter retail trade their costs, and the product costs, would rise. But we would always advise approaching the manufacturer if in doubt, or in search of the truth.

Do I have anything to fear from the authorities?

You should fear them in the Biblical sense of respecting them. In particular you should make sure that anything you do conforms to the Building Regulations, anything electrical to the Wiring Regulations, anything wet must meet with the approval of the water authority because they are responsible for a safe water supply. The present Building Regulations encompass structural matters, and fire risks, and there is someone at the Town Hall, usually the Building Inspector, who can interpret them. We mentioned that gas has its Gas Safety Regulations, and the gas people can speak for these.

It may seem rather a lot, but if you think of bypassing them, better check that your house insurance policy does not depend upon your conforming to the rules.

Anything else?

Yes. Good luck — and insulate well.

INDEX

121